THE COMPLETE MEDITERRANEAN DIET COOKBOOK FOR BEGINNERS

336 Days of Quick and Easy Recipes for Weight Loss to Regain Body Confidence and Life-changing Eating Habits with 12 Weeks Meal Plan

CAMILA WHITE

TABLE OF CONTENT

WHAT IS THE MEDITERRANEAN DIET?

The Mediterranean diet is an eating pattern that includes a variety of foods from countries around the Mediterranean Sea. The diet is based on the traditional foods that people ate in countries like Italy and Greece back in the 1960s.

The Mediterranean diet has been touted as one of the healthiest ways to eat, and for good reason. The diet emphasizes fruits, vegetables, whole grains, legumes, healthy fat nuts, and plenty of fish and wine (in moderation). Meats are eaten sparingly and only occasionally consumed.

This eating pattern has been shown to reduce risk factors for cardiovascular disease and other major health conditions such as diabetes. The Mediterranean diet also promotes lifelong healthy habits that are essential to living a longer life. Here's everything you need to know about this simple yet effective eating pattern.

BRIEF HISTORY OF THE MEDITERRANEAN DIET

The Mediterranean diet is a pattern of eating that is native to the countries surrounding the Mediterranean Sea. The exact origins of the diet are unknown, but it is thought to have begun in the 1960s.

The diet is based on the traditional foods that were eaten in countries like Italy and Greece. These countries have some of t world's lowest rates of heart disease and obesity.

The Mediterranean diet has been shown to improve heart health, weight loss, and blood sugar control. It also lowers inflammation, which can help reduce your risk for diseases like cancer and Alzheimer's. It is also known to decrease your risk of developing depression or anxiety.

MAJOR HEALTH BENEFITS OF THE MEDITERRANEAN DIET

The Mediterranean diet has been linked with a reduced risk of heart disease, arthritis, Alzheimer's disease, cancer, and diabetes. Studies have also shown that people who follow a Mediterranean diet have a lower risk of dying from all causes. In addition to the health benefits, the Mediterranean diet is also delicious and easy to follow.

With its focus on fresh fruits and vegetables, lean proteins, and healthy fats, you can't go wrong with this way of eating.

HERE ARE THE MAJOR HEALTH BENEFITS OF THIS DIET:

1. Lower risk of cardiovascular disease:

The Mediterranean diet has been shown to decrease the risk of heart disease. This could be because the diet is rich in healthy fats, antioxidants, and fiber. The diet has also been shown to lower cholesterol and blood pressure levels. All of these factors together help to keep your heart healthy and reduce your risk of developing heart disease. Heart disease is one of the biggest killers worldwide, but eating fruits and vegetables daily could dramatically reduce your risk.

More specifically, it lowers the risk of cardiovascular disease. Cardiovascular diseases refer to any condition that affects your heart or blood vessels. A few of these conditions include high blood pressure, coronary artery disease, atrial fibrillation, and stroke.

High blood pressure occurs when blood flows through your blood vessels more quickly than it should, resulting in thickened walls. This can make it more difficult for your heart to pump enough oxygen-rich blood to other parts of your body. Coronary artery disease refers to a narrowing of arteries due to plaque buildup, which reduces the amount of oxygen-rich blood being pumped from your heart throughout your body.

Meanwhile, atrial fibrillation is a condition in which your heart's upper chambers quiver rapidly instead of beating regularly. This can cause blood to pool and clot within your heart. A stroke occurs when a clot or another blockage cuts off blood flow to your brain, depriving it of oxygen-rich blood and essential nutrients needed for survival.

This med diet includes fruits, vegetables, whole grains, legumes, nuts, and seeds – a variety of healthy foods that can help you reduce inflammation and manage cholesterol levels.

Hence, a med diet helps to reduce the risk of different cardiovascular diseases. This is likely due to the high levels of antioxidants, healthy fats, and fiber found in this type of diet. The antioxidants help to protect against damage caused by free radicals, while the healthy fats help to reduce inflammation. The fiber helps to keep cholesterol levels in check and also helps to regulate blood sugar levels. Healthy gut bacteria are encouraged through a diet rich in olive oil, fruits, vegetables, legumes, nuts, and seeds; this supports good digestive health.

Studies have found that those who follow the Mediterranean diet have reduced levels of total cholesterol, low-density lipoprotein (LDL) cholesterol, triglycerides, blood pressure, and body weight. It has also been noted that those who followed this type of diet for at least five years had better results than those who only followed it for three months or less.

2. Lower risk of cancer:

Epidemiological studies suggest that adherence to the Mediterranean diet may be linked to a lower risk of breast cancer and prostate cancer. Eating foods like tomatoes, which contain lycopene, may be especially helpful in preventing prostate cancer. Other foods like olive oil, nuts, garlic, etc., which are staples in this type of diet offer protection against other types of cancers as well.

Studies have shown that a Mediterranean-style diet can reduce your cancer risk. One study found a 30% reduction in women's breast cancer rates when they followed this type of diet over eight years. The researchers behind this study think it may be because this type of eating plan limits certain foods that are thought to raise cancer risks like red meat, processed meats, high-fat dairy products, and sweets.

3. Lower risk of Alzheimer's disease:

Researchers believe that eating Mediterranean style may help prevent memory loss and decrease your risk of developing Alzheimer's disease by more than 50%.

Alzheimer's disease is a progressive brain disorder that causes loss of memory, thinking skills, and the ability to carry out daily activities. It also leads to confusion, mood swings, aggression, anxiety, and depression. It's not clear what causes Alzheimer's disease but scientists believe genetics may play a role along with lifestyle factors such as obesity or high blood pressure. However, there are some medications (such as cholinesterase inhibitors) that may delay the progression of Alzheimer's.

The typical Western diet has been linked to an increased risk of Alzheimer's disease, while the healthy fats found in a Mediterranean diet can help protect your brain. A recent study found that people who followed a Mediterranean diet had a 40% lower risk of developing Alzheimer's disease. Another study published in Neurology showed that those with the highest adherence to a Mediterranean-style diet had half the risk of dementia and Alzheimer's disease than those with low adherence.

Another key component of a Mediterranean diet is that it's rich in antioxidants, which can help prevent cell damage that contributes to Alzheimer's. This was shown in a study published in Neurology where researchers found that those who ate more fresh fruit and vegetables had up to 50% less risk of developing Alzheimer's disease than those who didn't.

4. It helps control diabetes:

The Mediterranean diet is recommended for people with diabetes because it reduces spikes in blood sugar levels after meals.

Studies show that people who follow a Med diet are less likely to develop type 2 diabetes. Type 2 diabetes occurs when your body can't make enough insulin or doesn't use insulin well. Insulin helps move glucose (sugar) out of your blood and into your cells where it's used for energy.

Glucose comes from the food you eat. The more sugar in your blood, the harder it is for your cells to do their job. If there isn't enough insulin or if cells become resistant to its effects, glucose builds up in your blood instead of going into cells.

Fortunately, one of the best benefits of following a Med diet is its ability to protect against type 2 diabetes. Diets high in fruits, vegetables, legumes, whole grains, and fish have all been found to be associated with a reduced risk for type 2 diabetes. It's not just about what you eat; it's also about how much you eat.

People who follow a Med diet typically don't overeat which means they aren't taking in excess calories or unhealthy fat which can lead to weight gain or obesity - both are major contributors to type 2 diabetes.

5) The Med diet reduces inflammation in the body

The benefits of the Mediterranean diet have been well-documented. This way of eating has been linked with a reduced risk of heart disease, cancer, Alzheimer's and Parkinson's disease, and other chronic conditions. The Med diet is also anti-inflammatory, meaning it can help to reduce inflammation in the body.

Chronic inflammation leads to many diseases including obesity, diabetes, arthritis, cardiovascular disease, depression, and more. Eating foods that are low on the glycemic index helps keep blood sugar levels under control.

The Med diet is also associated with a lower risk of arthritis and other inflammatory diseases. Studies have found that participants who followed this type of diet were less likely to suffer from rheumatoid arthritis than those who didn't. People who follow the Med diet tend to have lower levels of inflammation throughout their body, which may be one reason for these results.

SAUCES, DIPS, & DRESSINGS
GARLIC YOGURT SAUCE

Preparation time: 10 minutes; Cooking time: 5 minutes; Serves: 2 cups

Ingredients:

- ½ tsp. of kosher salt

- 1 tsp. of garlic powder

- 2 cups plain Greek yogurt that is low in fat (2%)

- 2 tbsp. of olive oil

- 4 tbsp. of freshly squeezed lemon juice

Instructions:

1. In a medium bowl, thoroughly combine all the ingredients.

2. Pour your yogurt sauce into a bowl, then store it in the fridge.

3. Until you're ready to serve, keep the covered bowl in the fridge for seven days.

4. Enjoy!

Nutritional Information:

Calories: 75; Carbohydrates: 3g; Fat: 5g; Fiber: 0g; Protein: 6g; Sodium: 173mg

BULGUR PILAF WITH ALMONDS

Preparation time: 10 minutes; Cooking time: 20 minutes; Serves: 6

Ingredients:

- 1/3 cup of sliced almonds

- 1/3 tsp. of salt

- ½ cup of chopped fresh cilantro

- 1 cup of uncooked bulgur

- 2 cups of water

- 1 ½ cup of small red bell pepper (diced)

- 1 ½ tbsp. of olive oil

Instructions:

1. In a saucepan, combine the bulgur and water, and then bring to a boil. When the water reaches a boil, put a lid on the pot and turn the heat off. Let the pot stand, covered, for 20 minutes.

2. Add the cooked bulgur, almonds, cilantro, peppers, salt, and oil to a sizable mixing bowl. To combine, stir.

3. Fill each of the four containers with roughly 1 cup of bulgur.

4. Before serving, keep covered containers inside the fridge for up to five days or till it is ready to be served. Bulgur tastes great at either room temperature or reheated.

5. Enjoy!

Nutritional Information:

Calories: 17; Carbohydrates: 25g; Fat: 7g; Fiber: 6g; Protein: 4g; Sodium: 152mg

ARTICHOKE-OLIVE COMPOTE

Preparation time: 5 minutes; Cooking time: 15 minutes; Serves: 2 cups

Ingredients:

- 2/3 cup of chopped & pitted green olives (8-9 olives)
- 1 tsp. of freshly squeezed lemon juice
- 2 (6-oz.) jars of chopped, marinated artichoke hearts
- 4 tsps. of olive oil
- 6 tbsps. of chopped fresh basil

Instructions:

1. In a medium-sized mixing bowl, combine all of the ingredients.

2. Put the compote inside a container and put it in the fridge.

3. Before Serving, keep sealed containers inside the fridge for seven days or till it is ready to be served.

4. Enjoy!

Nutritional Information:

Calories: 8; Carbohydrates: 5g; Fat: 7g; Fiber: 1g; Protein: 1g; Sodium: 350mg

ROSEMARY GARLIC

Preparation time: 5 minutes; Cooking time: 30 minutes; Serves: 2 cups

Ingredients:

- 2 cups of extra-virgin olive oil
- 8 large, smashed garlic cloves
- 8 sprigs of rosemary (4- to 5-inch)

Instructions:

1. Heat the ingredients in a medium skillet over low heat. Stirring occasionally, cook the garlic for 30 to 45 minutes or until it is fragrant and soft. Hot oil will cause the garlic to burn and turn bitter, so keep it from getting too hot.

2. Take the food off the heat and let it cool slightly. With a slotted spoon, take out the garlic and rosemary, then transfer the oil to a glass jar. Before covering, let the mixture cool completely.

3. Until you're ready to serve, keep covered at ambient temperature for as much as three months.

Nutritional Information:

Calories: 241; Carbohydrates: 1g; Fat: 26g; Fiber: 0g; Protein: 0g; Sodium: 1mg

SPANAKOPITA SAUCE

Preparation time: 15 minutes; Cooking time: 14 minutes; Serves: 4

Ingredients:

- ½ tsp. of ground nutmeg
- 1 tsp. of salt
- 1 lemon zest
- 2 tsps. of dried dill
- 4 minced garlic cloves
- 4 tbsps. of white onion (minced)
- 6 tbsps. of olive oil (divided)
- 8 cups of fresh spinach
- 8 oz. (113 g) of softened cream cheese
- 8 oz. (113 g) of divided feta cheese
- Olive oil cooking spray

For Serves: Pita chips, sliced bread, or carrot sticks (optional)

Instructions:

1. Set the air fryer's temperature to 360°F (182°C). Apply cooking spray olive oil inside a baking sheet or 6-inch baking dish.

2. Warm-up 1 tablespoon of olive oil in a sizable skillet on medium heat. Cook for about a minute after adding the onion.

3. Include the garlic, and cook for another minute while stirring.

4.   Turn the heat down to low and stir in the water and spinach. Cook the spinach for two or three minutes, or until it has wilted. Take the pan off the stove.

5.   Combine the lemon zest, dill, nutmeg, and salt in a medium bowl with 2 ounces of feta, cream cheese, and the unused 2 tablespoons of olive oil. Just combine after combining.

6.   Combine the cheese base with the vegetables after adding them.

7.   Add the sauce mixture to the pan that has been prepared and top with the final 2 oz. of feta cheese.

8.   Spoon the sauce into the air fryer's basket and heat or boil it for 10 minutes.

9.   Accompany with sliced bread, carrot sticks, or pita chips.

Nutritional Information:

Calories: 550; Carbohydrates: 9g; Fat: 52g; Fiber: 2g; Protein: 14g; Sodium: 113mg

HERB BUTTER

Preparation time: 5 minutes; Cooking time: 0 minutes; Serves: 1 cup

Ingredients:

- 1 cup of almond butter (room temperature)
- 1 tsp. of salt
- 2 finely minced garlic cloves
- 2 tsps. of fresh oregano (finely chopped)
- 4 tsps. of fresh rosemary (finely chopped)

Instructions:

1. Place all the ingredients in a food processor and process until well-combined, creamy, and smooth, scraping down the sides as necessary. Alternately, you could use an electric mixer to combine the ingredients.

2. Scrape the mixture of almond butter into a tiny glass bowl or container using a spatula, then cover.

3. Keep chilled for up to a month or until you're ready to serve.

Nutritional Information:

Calories: 103; Carbohydrates: 0g; Fat: 12g; Fiber: 0g; Protein: 0g; Sodium: 227mg

WALNUT PESTO

Preparation time: 5 minutes; Cooking time: 0 minutes; Serves: 6 cups

Ingredients:

- ¾ cup of chopped walnuts
- ¾ cup of extra-virgin olive oil
- ¾ cup of fresh rocket
- 1/3 cup of Parmesan cheese (shredded)
- 1/3 tsp. of salt
- 1½ garlic cloves (peeled)
- 4½ cups of packed arugula

Instructions:

1. Finely chop the rocket, walnuts, cheese, and garlic in a food processor. Then, season with salt. Pour the olive oil into the processor as it is operating and blend until smooth.

2. To make the mixture smooth and creamy, if it feels thick, pour in 1 tbsp. of lukewarm water at a time. Until you're ready to serve, keep in the it refrigerator in a closed container.

3. Enjoy!

Nutritional Information:

Calories: 296; Carbohydrates: 2g; Fat: 31g; Fiber: 1g; Protein: 4g; Sodium: 206mg

HONEY-LEMON VINAIGRETTE

Preparation time: 10 minutes; Cooking time: 5 minutes; Serves: 1 cup

Ingredients:

- ¼ tsp. of kosher salt
- ½ cup of lemon juice (freshly squeezed)
- ½ cup of olive oil
- 2 tsps. of honey
- 4 tsps. of Dijon mustard

Instructions:

1. In a small bowl, whisk together the salt, honey, mustard, and lemon juice.

2. Stir in the oil, then drizzle a thin stream of it into the bowl.

3. Transfer the vinaigrette to a container, then put it in the fridge.

4. Until you're ready to serve, keep the sealed container in the fridge for up to two weeks. Before serving, let the vinaigrette reach room temperature. Then shake and serve.

5. Enjoy!

Nutritional Information:

Calories: 131; Carbohydrates: 3g; Fat: 14g; Fiber: 1g; Protein: 1g; Sodium: 133mg

GREEN OLIVE AND SPINACH TAPENADE

Preparation time: 5 minutes; Cooking time: 20 minutes; Serves: 2 cups

Ingredients:

- 2/3 cup of fresh basil (packed)

- 1 tsp. of dried oregano

- 2 cups of drained pimento-stuffed green olives

- 4 tbsps. of olive oil

- 4 tsps. of chopped garlic

- 4 tsps. of red wine vinegar

- 6 packed cups of baby spinach

Instructions:

1.   Combine all your ingredients in a food processor's bowl and pulse several times until the mixture resembles finely chopped food that isn't puréed.

2.   Place the tapenade in a container and put it in the fridge.

3.   Before Serving, keep sealed containers inside the fridge for up to five days or till it's time to serve.

4.   Enjoy!

Nutritional Information:

Calories: 80; Carbohydrates: 1g; Fat: 8g; Fiber: 1g; Protein: 1g; Sodium: 6mg

FRUIT SALAD WITH MINT

Preparation time: 5 minutes; Cooking time: 10 minutes; Serves: 6 cups

Ingredients:

- ¾ tsp. of orange blossom water

- 3 cups of cantaloupe (cut into 1" cubes)

- 3 cups of hulled & halved strawberries

- 3 tbsps. of fresh mint (chopped)

Instructions:

1. Combine all the ingredients in a large bowl.

2. Fill each of the five containers with one cup of fruit salad.

3. Before Serving, keep sealed containers inside the fridge for up to five days, or until you are ready to serve.

Nutritional Information:

Calories: 52; Carbohydrates: 12g; Fat: 1g; Fiber: 2g; Protein: 1g; Sodium: 10mg

PIEMONTESE SAUCE

Preparation time: 5 minutes; Cooking time: 20 minutes; Serves: 6 cups

Ingredients:

- 1/3 cup of extra-virgin olive oil

- 1/3 tsp. of black pepper (freshly ground)

- 1/3 tsp. of salt

- 3 garlic cloves (large and finely minced)

- 3 tbsps. (½ stick) of butter (optional)

- 6 anchovy fillets (very finely chopped)

Instructions:

1. Heat the butter (optional) and olive oil inside a small saucepan. Allow medium-low heat to melt the butter.

2. Toss in the garlic and anchovies then season with pepper and salt before reducing to low heat.

3. Cook on low heat for about 20 minutes and stir occasionally until the anchovies soften and give off a unique fragrance.

4. Top with steamed veggies as a sort of dip for the cooked artichokes, raw veggies, or salad dressing. Serve hot.

5. Place the leftovers in a sealed, airtight container and store them in the freezer for as long as 2 weeks or whenever you are ready to serve.

Nutritional Information:

Calories: 181; Carbohydrates: 1g; Fat: 20g; Fiber: 0g; Protein: 1g; Sodium: 333mg

TAHINI DRESSING
Preparation time: 5 minutes; Cooking time: 0 minutes; Serves: 6

Ingredients:

- 1/3 cup of tahini
- ¼ cup of extra-virgin olive oil
- ¼ cup of lemon juice (freshly squeezed from 2 or 3 lemons)
- ¾ garlic clove (finely minced) or ½ tsp. of garlic powder
- 1½ tsps. of salt

Instructions:

1. Mix all the ingredients in a glass jar.

2. Put the lid on and shake until you get a smooth and creamy mixture.

3. Refrigerate for as long as 2 weeks or until whenever you are ready to serve.

Nutritional Information:

Calories: 121; Carbohydrates: 2g; Fat: 12g; Fiber: 1g; Protein: 2g; Sodium: 479mg

TZATZIKI SAUCE
Preparation time: 5 minutes; Cooking time: 0 minutes; Serves: 4

Ingredients:

- 1 cup of full-fat Greek yogurt (plain and unsweetened)
- 1 juiced lemon
- 1 tsp. of dried dill
- 1 tsp. of garlic (dried and minced)
- 1 tsp. of salt (divided, add to taste)
- 2 medium-sized cucumbers (peeled, seeded, & diced)
- 2 tbsps. of fresh parsley (chopped)
- Black pepper, freshly ground (to taste)

Instructions:

1.   Place the diced cucumbers inside a colander and season with ¼ tsp. of salt before mixing. Allow the cucumbers to remain there for 30 minutes at room temperature.

2.   Drop the cucumbers into cold water; rinse and place in one layer on stacked paper towels to drain the excess water.

3.   Place the cucumbers in a food processor and blend until it is finely chopped.

4.   Remove the excess liquid and pour it into a bowl. Add the lemon juice, yogurt, garlic, dill, parsley, and leftover ¼ tsp. of salt. Add pepper and salt to taste and blend.

5.   Store in an airtight container and place in a freezer until you are ready to serve.

Nutritional Information:

Calories: 77; Carbohydrates: 6g; Fat: 3g; Fiber: 1g; Protein: 6g; Sodium: 607mg

BREAKFAST

BANANA CORN FRITTERS

Preparation time: 5 minutes; Cooking time: 10 minutes; Serves: 4

Ingredients:

- ½ cup of flour
- ½ to ½ tsp. of ground chipotle chili
- ½ tsp. of ground cinnamon
- ½ tsp. of sea salt
- 1 cup of yellow cornmeal
- 1 tsp. of baking powder
- 2 large eggs (beaten)
- 2 tbsps. of olive oil
- 4 small bananas (ripe, peeled, & mashed)
- 4 tbsps. of almond milk (unsweetened)

Instructions:

1. Set aside the olive oil and mix the remaining ingredients inside a large bowl until you get a smooth mixture.

2. Let a non-stick skillet heat over medium-high heat before adding the olive oil and about 2 tbsps. of batter to each fritter.

3. Allow to cook for 2 or 3 minutes and flip when the bottoms turn a golden brown color.

4. Cook for additional 1 or 2 minutes.

5.   Repeat this process with the other remaining batter.

6.   Best served warm.

Nutritional Information:

Calories: 396; Carbohydrates: 68g; Fat: 10g; Fiber: 4g; Protein: 7g; Sodium: 307mg

SWEET POTATO TOAST

Preparation time: 5 minutes; Cooking time: 15 minutes; Serves: 6

Ingredients:

- 1½ cup of arugula

- 1½ cup of fresh spinach

- 12 medium asparagus (trimmed)

- 3 plum tomatoes (halved)

- 3 sweet potatoes (large and sliced lengthwise)

- 6 large cooked eggs or any egg substitute (scrambled, poached, or fried)

- 6 tbsps. of Asiago cheese (shredded)

- 6 tbsps. of pesto

- 9 tbsps. of extra-virgin olive oil (divided)

- Black pepper (freshly ground, to taste)

- Salt (to taste)

Instructions:

1.	Preheat your oven to 230°C (450°F. or Fan 210°C).

2.	Place the halves of plum tomato on a baking sheet and brush them with 2 tbsps. of olive oil. Season with pepper and salt then place in the oven to roast for about 15 minutes. Take it out of the oven and leave it to rest.

3.	Get another baking sheet and place the slices of sweet potato on it. Brush each side with approximately 2 tbsps. of oil and season with pepper and salt. Bake in an oven for approximately 15 minutes, flipping every 5-7 minutes. Once it is tender, take it out and set it aside.

4.   Heat the leftover 2 tbsps. of olive oil in a skillet or sauté pan placed on medium heat. Add the fresh spinach to the sauté just until it wilts. Then take out the pan and sit on a dish lined with a paper towel to rest. Sauté the asparagus in the pan, turning continuously allow it to drain on a dish lined with a paper towel.

5.   On each serving plate, place the grilled sweet potato slices; evenly divide the asparagus and spinach among the slices, then place an egg on top before topping with the ¼ cup arugula.

6.   Drizzle a tablespoon of pesto and a tablespoon of cheese.

7.   Serve alongside a roasted plum tomato.

Nutritional Information:

Calories: 441; Carbohydrates: 23g; Fat: 35g; Fiber: 4g; Protein: 13g; Sodium: 481mg

CHEESE FRITTATA WITH VEGETABLES

Preparation time: 15 minutes; Cooking time: 25 minutes; Serves: 4

Ingredients:

- 1 pint of cherry or grape tomatoes
- 1 tsp. of salt
- 10 large eggs (beaten)
- 2 tbsps. of olive oil
- 4 garlic cloves (minced)
- 4 oz. (57 g) of crumbled goat cheese (approximately ½ cup)
- 4 tbsps. of fresh basil (minced)
- 4 tbsps. of fresh oregano (minced)
- 6 tbsps. of unsweetened almond milk
- Pinch of freshly ground black pepper

Instructions:

1.   Place your non-stick skillet with oil in it over medium heat. Add tomatoes and allow to cook while piercing some of them to release some juice. Decrease to medium-low heat, then cover your pan to allow the tomatoes to get soft.

2.   Take off the lid after your tomatoes are well broken down, add garlic, and leave to sauté.

3.   Mix the eggs, milk, herbs, pepper, and salt in a medium-sized bowl and whisk properly.

4.   Increase the heat to medium-high and pour the egg mixture into the tomato mixture.

5.   Sprinkle the eggs with goat cheese then cover the pan to allow the mixture to cook for approximately 7 minutes.

6.   Remove the pan's cover and allow to cook for additional 7-10 minutes.

7.   Once the eggs are set and the spatula doesn't stick to the edges of the pan, allow the frittata to cool down for approximately 5 minutes.

8.   Cut into wedges then serve.

Nutritional Information:

Calories: 417; Carbohydrates: 12g; Fat: 31g; Fiber: 3g; Protein: 26g; Sodium: 867mg

GREEN SMOOTHIE

Preparation time: 10 minutes; Cooking time: 0 minutes; Serves: 2

Ingredients:

- 1 medium cucumber (peeled & seeded)

- 16-10 fresh mint leaves without stems

- 2 cups of almond milk or water (as required)

- 2 cups of tender leaves of baby spinach without the stems

- 2 small avocados (very ripe, peeled, & pitted)

- 2 tbsps. of extra-virgin olive oil (alternatively, use avocado oil)

- 2 to 2 tbsps. of juice (from 1 lime)

Instructions:

1.   Mix the avocado, spinach, almond milk, cucumber, mint, lime juice, and olive oil in an immersion blender's wide-mouth jar or a regular blender. Blend until it is creamy and smooth.

2.   To get your preferred consistency, pour in more almond milk or some water.

3.   When it's ready, serve.

Nutritional Information:

Calories: 330; Carbohydrates: 19g; Fat: 30g; Fiber: 8g; Protein: 4g; Sodium: 36mg

PANCAKES WITH BERRY SAUCE

Preparation time: 5 minutes; Cooking time: 10 minutes; Serves: 6

Ingredients:

- 1/3 tsp. of salt

- ¾ tsp. of vanilla extract

- 1 lemon (extract zest and juice)

- 1½ cup of almond flour

- 1½ tsp. of baking powder

- 3 large eggs (beaten)

- 9 tbsps. of extra-virgin olive oil (divided)

Berry Sauce:

- 1½ cup of frozen mixed berries

- 1½ tbsps. of water (add more if required)

Instructions:

1.   Stir the baking powder, almond flour, and salt in a big bowl until there are no lumps.

2.   Stir in 4 tbsps. of olive oil, lemon zest & juice, beaten eggs, and the vanilla extract until they are properly mixed.

3.   Pour 1 tbsp. of olive oil into a large skillet to heat up. Add 2 tbsps. of batter to each pancake and cook for about 4-5 minutes until you notice bubbles forming. Flip the pancake and cook for an additional 2-3 minutes. Repeat the process with the batter and leftover 1 tbsp. of olive oil.

Berry Sauce:

4.   Mix the frozen berries, vanilla extract, and water in a small-sized saucepan. Place over medium-high heat and allow to heat for 3-4 minutes. As it gets bubbly, add water as required. Use the back of a fork or spoon to mash the berries, then whisk to smoothen.

5.   Serve pancakes alongside the berry sauce.

Nutritional Information:

Calories: 275; Carbohydrates: 8g; Fat: 26g; Fiber: 2g; Protein: 4g; Sodium: 271mg

CARDAMOM-CINNAMON OATS

Preparation time: 10 minutes; Cooking time: 0 minutes; Serves: 4

Ingredients:

- ½ tsp. of ground cardamom
- ½ tsp. of ground cinnamon
- 1 cup of rolled oats
- 1 cup of vanilla (unsweetened almond milk - not Silk brand)
- 2 tsps. of chia seeds
- 4 tbsps. of simple sugar liquid sweetener
- 4 tbsps. of sliced almonds

Instructions:

1. Mix the almond milk, chia seeds, almonds, oats, cinnamon, liquid sweetener, and cardamom together inside a mason jar.

2. Shake very well and refrigerate for about 8-24 hours.

3. Serve heated or cold when ready.

Nutritional Information:

Calories: 131; Carbohydrates: 17g; Fat: 6g; Fiber: 4g; Protein: 5g; Sodium: 45mg

GREEK YOGURT WITH NUTS

Preparation time: 10 minutes; Cooking time: 0 minutes; Serves: 4

Ingredients:

- 1 cup of frozen berries (thawed with juices)

- 1 tsp. of ground cinnamon (optional)

- 2 cups of plain, whole-milk Greek yogurt

- 2 tsps. of almond or vanilla extract (optional)

- 4 tbsps. of ground flaxseeds

- 8 tbsps. of chopped nuts (pecans or walnuts)

- 8 tbsps. of heavy whipping cream

Instructions:

1. Mix the yogurt, thawed berries inside their juices, heavy whipping cream, cinnamon (if using), almond or vanilla extract (if using), and flaxseed in a small glass or bowl. Stir until the mixture is smooth.

2. Top the mixture with chopped nuts.

3. Serve and enjoy.

Nutritional Information:

Calories: 267; Carbohydrates: 12g; Fat: 19g; Fiber: 3g; Protein: 11g; Sodium: 63mg

BULGUR BOWLS WITH FRUITS

Preparation time: 5 minutes; Cooking time: 15 minutes; Serves: 8

Ingredients:

- 1/3 cup of loosely packed fresh mint (chopped)

- 2/3 cup of chopped almonds

- 2/3 tsp. of ground cinnamon

- 1 1/3 cups of water

- 2 cups of uncooked bulgur

- 2 2/3 cups of frozen, fresh, or pitted dark sweet cherries

- 2 2/3 cups of unsweetened almond milk

- 10 2/3 dried or fresh chopped figs

Instructions:

1.   In a medium-sized saucepan, stir in the milk, cinnamon, bulgur, and water and bring to a boil.

2.   Reduce to medium-low heat, cover the saucepan, and let it simmer for about 10 minutes to allow the mixture to absorb the liquid.

3.   With the pan still on the stove, turn the heat off and add the frozen cherries without thawing, almonds, and figs. Stir and cover for a minute to allow the hot bulgur to hydrate the figs partially and thaw the cherries.

4.   Fold the mint in and stir well.

5.   Serve and enjoy.

Nutritional Information:

Calories: 207; Carbohydrates: 32g; Fat: 6g; Fiber: 4g; Protein: 8g; Sodium: 82mg

BRUSCHETTA WITH PROSCIUTTO

Preparation time: 10 minutes; Cooking time: 20 minutes; Serves: 6

Ingredients:

- 1/3 tsp. of black pepper (freshly ground)

- 1/3 tsp. of red pepper (crushed)

- 1/3 tsp. of sea salt or kosher

- 1½ garlic cloves (halved)

- 1½ oz. (28 g) of prosciutto (cut into ½" pieces)

- 1½ tbsps. of extra-virgin olive oil

- 1½ tbsps. of unsweetened almond milk

- 3 minced garlic cloves (about 1 tsp.)

- 4½ large eggs

- 6 tsps. of grated Parmesan (or Pecorino Romano) cheese

- 9 cups of broccoli rabe (about 1 bunch; stemmed and chopped)

- 12 (¾-inch thick) slices of whole-grain bread (baguette-style) or 4 slices of larger whole-grain bread (Italian-style)

- Nonstick cooking spray

Instructions:

1.   Pour water into a large stockpot and bring to a boil. Add broccoli rabe and salt then let it boil for about 2 minutes. Place inside a colander to drain.

2.   Place a large skillet with oil over medium heat. Allow heating then add the prosciutto, crushed red pepper, and garlic. Stir often and let it cook for about 2 minutes. Stir in the broccoli rabe and let it cook for 3 minutes extra. Place it in a bowl and keep it aside.

3.   Return the skillet to the stove; place it on low heat and use non-stick cooking spray to coat it.

4.   Whisk the eggs, pepper, and milk together inside a small bowl. Pour the mixture into the skillet, then stir and cook for 3-5 minutes until the eggs become scrambled and soft. Add the cheese and mixture of broccoli rabe to the skillet, stir, and cook for a minute. After heating through, take it off the heat.

5.   Toast your bread, and rub the halves of the garlic clove (the cut sides) on each side of the toasted bread. Spread the egg mixture on each piece of the toasted bread and serve.

Nutritional Information:

Calories: 313; Carbohydrates: 38g; Fat: 10g; Fiber: 8g; Protein: 17g; Sodium: 559mg

RICOTTA WITH HONEY

Preparation time: 5 minutes; Cooking time: 25 minutes; Serves: 6

Ingredients:

- 1/3 cup of whole-wheat pastry flour
- 1/3 tsp. of ground nutmeg
- 1½ tbsps. of honey
- 1½ tbsps. of sugar
- 1½ tsps. of vanilla extract
- 1½ (1 lb. or 454 g) container of whole-milk ricotta cheese
- 1½ of cored and diced pear
- 3 large eggs
- 3 tbsps. of water
- Nonstick cooking spray

Instructions:

1.   Preheat your oven to 200°C (400°F or Fan 180°C) then spray nonstick cooking spray on 4 ramekins.

2.   In a big bowl, beat the eggs, ricotta, flour, nutmeg, vanilla, and sugar until well mixed.

3.   Put the mixture inside the ramekins.

4.   Place in a preheated oven to bake for 22-25 minutes, and ensure your ricotta is set.

5.   Pour water into a small saucepan on a stove set on medium heat. Place the pear inside and let it simmer for 10 minutes. When it softens slightly, take it off the heat, add the honey, and stir.

6.   Take out the ramekins and place them on a wire rack to cool a bit. Top with the pear. Serve and enjoy.

Nutritional Information:

Calories: 329; Carbohydrates: 23g; Fat: 19g; Fiber: 3g; Protein: 17g; Sodium: 109mg

POACHED EGGS

Preparation time: 5 minutes; Cooking time: 15 minutes; Serves: 4

Ingredients:

- 4 large eggs

- 1 1/3 garlic cloves (minced)

- 1/3 cup of fresh flat-leaf parsley (chopped)

- 2/3 tbsp. of extra-virgin olive oil

- 2/3 cup of chopped onion

- 1 1/3 (14.5 oz. or 411 g) cans of Italian diced tomatoes (no-salt-added and not drained)

Instructions:

1. Pour olive oil into a large skillet and place over medium-high heat.

2. Sauté the onions in the heated oil for 5 minutes. Stir from time to time and add the garlic. Let it cook for an additional 1 minute.

3. Add the tomatoes and the juices to the oil and cook for 2-3 minutes or until it begins to bubble.

4. Turn down the heat to medium and indent the tomato mixture into 6 places with a large spoon.

5. Crack each of the eggs into individual indentations.

6. Cover the skillet and leave to simmer for about 6-7 minutes.

7.   Once the eggs are cooked to your preferred taste, serve and sprinkle the parsley on them.

Nutritional Information:

Calories: 89; Carbohydrates: 4g; Fat: 6g; Fiber: 1g; Protein: 4g; Sodium: 77mg

BLUEBERRY AND CHIA SEEDS SMOOTHIE

Preparation time: 10 minutes; Cooking time: 0 minutes; Serves: 2

Ingredients:

- ½ cup of frozen blueberries

- ½ tsp. of ground cinnamon

- 1 tsp. of vanilla extract

- 2 cups of unsweetened almond milk (add more if needed)

- 2 tbsps. of avocado oil or extra-virgin olive oil

- 2 tbsps. of ground chia seeds or flaxseed

- 2 tsps. monk fruit or stevia extract (optional)

- 4 tbsps. of unsweetened almond butter

Instructions:

1.   Put all the ingredients inside a blender or in a big wide-mouth jar, if you're using an immersion blender. Blend to a creamy and smooth consistency.

2.   You can add more almond milk until you have your preferred consistency.

3.   Serve when you're done.

Nutritional Information:

Calories: 460; Carbohydrates: 20g; Fat: 40g; Fiber: 9g; Protein: 8g; Sodium: 147mg

ORANGE FRENCH TOAST

Preparation time: 5 minutes; Cooking time: 15 minutes; Serves: 4

Ingredients:

- 1/8 cup of Berry & Honey Compote
- 1/8 tsp. of ground cardamom
- 1/8 tsp. of ground cinnamon
- 2/3 cup of unsweetened almond milk
- 2/3 inch thick (preferably gluten-free)
- 2/3 loaf of sliced boule bread
- 2/3 sliced banana
- 2/3 tsp. of vanilla extract
- 1 1/3 tsp. of orange zest (grated)
- 2 large eggs

Instructions:

1.   Set your stove on medium-high heat and place a big non-stick skillet or normal skillet on it to heat.

2.   Get a large but shallow container and mix the eggs, milk, orange zest, cinnamon, vanilla, and cardamom in it.

3.   Batch by batch, dip the bread slices into the egg mixture before placing it inside the heated pan.

4.   Cook each side for 5 minutes, until it turns golden brown.

5. Place in a serving dish. Garnish with banana and use the honey compote as a topping.

Nutritional Information:

Calories: 394; Carbohydrates: 68g; Fat: 6g; Fiber: 3g; Protein: 17g; Sodium: 716mg

VANILLA RASPBERRY OATS

Preparation time: 10 minutes; Cooking time: 0 minutes; Serves: 4

Ingredients:

- ¼ tsp. of ground cinnamon
- ²/₃ cup of vanilla (unsweetened almond milk)
- ¹/₃ cup of rolled oats
- ½ cup of raspberries
- ½ tsp. of turmeric
- 2 tsps. of honey
- Pinch of ground cloves

Instructions:

1. Mix all the ingredients inside a mason jar and shake properly.

2. Refrigerate for up to 8 – 24 hours.

3. Can be served cold or hot.

Nutritional Information:

Calories: 82; Carbohydrates: 14g; Fat: 2g; Fiber: 3g; Protein: 2g; Sodium: 98mg

AVOCADO WITH EGGS TOAST
Preparation time: 5 minutes; Cooking time: 7 minutes; Serves: 6

Ingredients:

- 1½ avocado
- 6 large eggs
- 6 pieces of whole grain bread
- Olive oil cooking spray
- Red pepper flakes (optional)
- Salt & black pepper (to taste)

Instructions:

1. Make the air fryer preheat to 160ºC or 320ºF.

2. Get four small-sized baking molds and use olive oil cooking spray to coat the insides lightly.

3. Break one egg in each mold then use black pepper and salt to season.

4. Put the baking molds inside the air fryer basket and close. Set timer to seven minutes.

5. While waiting for the eggs to be ready, place the bread inside a toaster to toast.

6. Divide your avocado in half (lengthwise); take out the stone, and scoop out the pulp into a small-sized bowl. Season your avocado with

black pepper, salt, and red pepper flakes (optional). Then use a fork to mash the avocado lightly.

7. Evenly spread a quarter of your mashed avocado over each toasted bread slice.

8. Get the eggs out of the deep fryer and place an egg on each bread slice.

9. Serve and enjoy.

Nutritional Information:

Calories: 232; Carbohydrates: 18g; Fat: 14g; Fiber: 6g; Protein: 11g; Sodium: 175mg

FISH AND SEAFOOD
SALMON WITH TOMATOES
Preparation time: 5 minutes; Cooking time: 8 minutes; Serves: 6

Ingredients:

- ¾ tsp. of salt

- 1/3 cup of Kalamata olives (sliced)

- 1/3 tsp. of cayenne

- 1½ tsp. of fresh dill (chopped)

- 3 diced Roma tomatoes

- 3 tbsps. of olive oil

- 6 salmon fillets (1½" thick)

- 6 slices of lemon

Instructions:

1.   Let the air fryer preheat to 375oF.

2.   Brush both sides of your salmon fillets with olive oil and use cayenne, dill, and salt to lightly season them.

3.   Place each fillet in the air fryer basket in a single layer. Layer with tomatoes and olives and top with a slice of lemon.

4.   Bake it for 8 minutes and stop when the internal temperature of the salmon reaches 63ºC (145ºF).

5.   Serve and enjoy.

Nutritional Information:

Calories: 241; Carbohydrates: 3g; Fat: 15g; Fiber: 1g; Protein: 23g; Sodium: 595mg

ROASTED SHRIMP-GNOCCHI BAKE
Preparation time: 10 minutes; Cooking time: 20 minutes; Serves: 6

Ingredients:

- ¾ cup of feta cheese (cubed)

- ¾ tsp. of black pepper (freshly ground)

- ¹/₃ cup of basil leaves (fresh torn)

- 1/3 tsp. of red pepper (crushed)

- 1½ (12 oz. or 340 g) jar of roasted red peppers (drained & coarsely chopped)

- 1½ cup of fresh tomato (chopped)

- 1½ lb. (454 g) of unthawed frozen gnocchi

- 1½ pound (454 g) fresh raw shrimp (frozen or thawed shrimp) with the shells & tails removed

- 3 minced garlic cloves

- 3 tbsps. of extra-virgin olive oil

Instructions:

1. Let your oven preheat to 400°F (200°C or Fan 180°C).

2. Combine the tomatoes, garlic, chopped red pepper, oil, and garlic inside a baking dish and place in the oven to roast for 10 minutes.

3. Add the shrimp and roasted peppers then stir. Leave to roast for additional 10 minutes and let the shrimp's color change to pink and white.

4.   As the shrimps are still cooking, place the gnocchi to cook on the stove and follow the package instructions. Let the colander drain then keep it warm.

5.   Take the pan out of the oven. Serve with the cooked gnocchi, feta, and basil.

Nutritional Information:

Calories: 146; Carbohydrates: 1g; Fat: 4g; Fiber: 0g; Protein: 23g; Sodium: 1144mg

LEMON ROSEMARY BRANZINO

Preparation time: 15 minutes; Cooking time: 30 minutes; Serves: 4

Ingredients:

- 1 cup of dry white wine

- 1 cup of sliced pitted Kalamata or other good-quality black olives

- 1 tbsp. of ground chili pepper (Turkish or Aleppo preferably)

- 2 bunch of scallions (just the white part and thinly sliced)

- 2 large carrots (cut into ¼ -inch rounds)

- 2 minced garlic cloves

- 2 small lemons (very thinly sliced)

- 20 – 12 small cherry tomatoes (halved)

- 4 (8 oz. or 227 g) branzino fillets (preferably at least 1" thick)

- 4 rosemary sprigs or 1 tbsp. of dried rosemary

- 4 tbsps. of paprika

- 4 tsps. of kosher salt

- 8 tbsps. of extra-virgin olive oil (divided)

Instructions:

1.   Place a skillet that is large and oven-safe over high heat for about 2 minutes. When it gets hot, add 1 tbsp. of olive oil carefully and let it glisten in about 10-15 seconds. Place the sea bass fillets with the skin side up for about 2 minutes to brown before flipping them and cooking for additional 2 minutes. When you are done, set them aside.

2.   Evenly coat the pan by shaking 2 tbsps. of olive oil around it. Then sauté the shallots, garlic, carrot, tomatoes, and kalamata olives in it for 5 minutes. When they get soft, stir in the wine and keep stirring to properly integrate the ingredients. Place your fish in the vegetable sauce carefully.

3. Let your oven preheat to 450°F (230°C or Fan 210°C).

4. As the oven heats up, use 1 tbsp. of olive oil to brush the fillets then season with salt, chili, and paprika. Use the rosemary sprig and lemon slices to garnish each fillet then sprinkle the fish and pan with the olives.

5. Let it roast for approximately 10 minutes until the edges of the lemon are charred or golden.

6. Serve and enjoy.

Nutritional Information:

Calories: 725; Carbohydrates: 25g; Fat: 43g; Fiber: 10g; Protein: 58g; Sodium: 2954mg

FAST SEAFOOD PAELLA

Preparation time: 20 minutes; Cooking time: 20 minutes; Serves: 6

Ingredients:

- ¾ cup of frozen peas

- 1/3 cup of plus 1 tbsp. of extra-virgin olive oil

- ¹/₃ lb. (136 g) of calamari rings

- 1½ cup of dry white wine

- 1½ finely chopped large onion

- 1½ halved lemon

- 1½ tbsps. of sweet paprika

- 12 oz. (227 g) of canned crab or lobster meat

- 2¼ cups of medium-grain Spanish paella rice (or arborio rice)

- 2¼ tbsps. of garlic powder

- 3 finely diced carrots

- 3 tomatoes (peeled & chopped)

- 4½ cups of chicken stock (add more as required)

- 9 jumbo shrimp (unpeeled)

- Salt (to taste)

Instructions:

1.   Set the stove on medium heat and pour the oil in a preferably 16-inch large skillet to heat until it starts forming small bubbles. Cook the onion in it for approximately 3 minutes until it gets fragrant. Add the garlic powder and tomatoes and cook for 5 to 10 minutes to allow your tomatoes to reduce by half and get a sticky consistency.

2.   Add the rice, paprika, carrots, lobster, peas, and salt and mix properly. Heat the chicken broth inside in a bowl or pot that is microwave-safe and bring to almost a boil. Add the mixture into the rice mixture and bring to a boil before adding the wine.

3.   Smoothen the rice at the pan's bottom, cover it and allow to cook for 10 minutes over low heat. Stir from time to time so it doesn't get burnt.

4.   Use prawns to cover the rice then cover and allow to cook for extra 5 minutes. Pour in more broth if the rice is getting dry.

5.   Add squid rings to the pan before taking it off the heat. Stir frequently until the rings start to look dull after about 2 minutes. Take the pan off the heat to prevent the paella from overcooking. Squeeze in the fresh lemon juice.

6.   Serve and enjoy.

Nutritional Information:

Calories: 632; Carbohydrates: 71g; Fat: 20g; Fiber: 5g; Protein: 34g; Sodium: 920mg

FIDEOS WITH SEAFOOD

Preparation time: 15 minutes; Cooking time: 20 minutes; Serves: 8

Ingredients:

- 2/3 cup of feta cheese (crumbled)
- 2/3 cup of goat cheese (crumbled)
- 2/3 cup of Parmesan cheese (shredded)
- 2/3 tsp. of smoked paprika
- 11/3 (28 oz. or 794 g) can of chopped tomatoes (with the juices)
- 11/3 lb. (454 g) of peeled, deveined, & roughly chopped shrimp
- 11/3 tsps. of garlic powder
- 11/3 tsps. of salt
- 22/3 tbsps. of extra-virgin olive oil, plus 1/2 cup, divided
- 5 1/3 oz. (113 g) of crab meat
- 8 cups of zucchini noodles (2 – 3 medium zucchini, roughly chopped
- 8 to 8 oz. (170 – 227 g) of canned chopped clams (drained)
- For garnish: 1/3 cup of fresh flat-leaf Italian parsley (chopped)

Instructions:

1. Let your oven preheat to 375°F (190°C or Fan 170°C).

2. Pour 2 tbsps. of olive oil in a 9 x 13" pan. Coat the bottom by shaking it.

3. Mix the prawns, courgette noodles, crab meat, and clams inside a large bowl.

4.   Get another bowl and mix the feta, 1 cup of olive oil, and goat cheese properly. Add salt, the canned tomatoes with the juices, paprika, and garlic powder. Put this mixture in the courgette mixture and toss them to combine.

5.   Distribute the mixture evenly in the pan and spread the Parmesan and ¼ cup of olive oil on top. Cook for 20 – 30 minutes until it boils.

6.   Garnish with the chopped parsley and serve hot.

Nutritional Information:

Calories: 434; Carbohydrates: 12g; Fat: 31g; Fiber: 3g; Protein: 29g; Sodium: 712mg

GARLIC SHRIMP BLACK BEAN PASTA
Preparation time: 10 minutes; Cooking time: 15 minutes; Serves: 6

Ingredients:

- 1/3 cup of basil (cut into strips)

- 1½ lb. (454 g) of fresh shrimp (peeled & deveined)

- 1½ lb. (454 g) of black bean linguine (or spaghetti)

- 1½ onion (finely chopped)

- 4½ minced garlic cloves

- 6 tbsps. of extra-virgin olive oil

Instructions:

1.   Boil a large pot of water and follow the instructions on the pasta's package to cook it.

2.   When it's 5 minutes left to cook the pasta, throw in the prawns and allow to cook for 3 to 5 minutes. After they've turned pink, take them out of the hot water, running them through cold water if they are hot. Put it aside.

3.   Reserve a cup of the cooking water from the pasta and heat the oil inside the same pan over medium-high heat. Cook the garlic and onion for 7 to 10 minutes, then add the pasta when the onion becomes translucent. Mix properly.

4.   Serve garnished with the basil and prawns.

Nutritional Information:

Calories: 668; Carbohydrates: 73g; Fat: 19g; Fiber: 31g; Protein: 57g; Sodium: 615mg

FISH FILLET ON LEMONS
Preparation time: 5 minutes; Cooking time: 6 minutes; Serves: 6

Ingredients:

• 1/3 tsp. of black pepper (freshly ground)

• 1/3 tsp. of sea salt or kosher

• 1½ tsps. of extra-virgin olive oil

• 4½ to 4 medium lemons

• 6 (4 oz. or 113 g) of fish fillets (including tilapia, catfish, salmon, cod, or any other fish)

• Nonstick cooking spray

Instructions:

1. Use paper towels to dry the fillets then allow them to rest for 10 minutes at room temperature. In the meantime, use the non-stick cooking spray to coat your cold grill cooking rack. Preheat the grill on the stove over medium-high heat or to 205ºC (400ºF).

2. Cut the lemon into 2 halves and set one half aside. Cut the half into ¼-inch-thick slices until you get 12 to 16 slices of lemon. Squeeze out a tbsp. of juice from the other lemon half into a small bowl.

3. Mix the oil with the lemon juice in the bowl. Use the oil mixture to brush the two sides of the fish then use pepper and salt to sprinkle evenly.

4. Arrange the slices of lemon on the grill pan or grill carefully. Arrange 3 or 4 lemon slices in a fish fillet shape. Do the same with the other slices. Keep the fish fillets on the slices of lemon, close the lid and grill. However, use an aluminum foil or large lid as ca over if you are using a stove to grill. Halfway through cooking time, turn the fish over if the fish fillets exceed ½ an inch thick.

5.   When the fish starts separating into pieces or flakes when you press gently with a fork, then it's ready to serve.

Nutritional Information:

Calories: 208; Carbohydrates: 2g; Fat: 11g; Fiber: 0g; Protein: 21g; Sodium: 249mg

FISH AND ORZO

Preparation time: 10 minutes; Cooking time: 35 minutes; Serves: 6

Ingredients:

- 1½ cup of orzo pasta
- 1½ oz. of crumbled feta cheese
- 1½ tbsps. of chopped parsley
- 1½ tbsps. of olive oil
- 1½ tsp. of crushed red pepper
- 1½ tsp. of minced garlic
- 3 chopped shallots
- 3 tbsps. of chopped oregano
- 3 tbsps. of drained capers
- 3 tbsps. of pitted and chopped black olives
- 3 tsps. of anchovy paste
- 4½ cups of chicken stock
- 6 boneless cod fillets
- 22½ oz. of crushed canned tomatoes
- Black pepper
- Pinch of salt
- Zest of 1 lemon (grated)

Instructions:

1.   Heat the oil over medium heat and add the chili, shallot, and garlic then sauté for up to 5 minutes.

2.   Add the black olives, anchovy paste, oregano, tomatoes, capers, pepper, and salt. Combine and let it cook for an additional 5 minutes.

3.   Add the cod fillets, and sprinkle with parsley and cheese. Set the oven to cook for an additional 15 minutes at 375°F.

4.   Add the broth to the saucepan and let it boil on medium heat. Add the lemon zest and barley then let it cook and boil for 10 minutes. Use a fork to shell and divide it into plates.

5.   Use the fish mixture to top the portions.

6.   Serve and enjoy.

Nutritional Information:

Calories: 402; Carbohydrates: 21g; Fat: 21g; Fiber: 8g; Protein: 31g

CRISPY FRIED SARDINES
Preparation time: 5 minutes; Cooking time: 5 minutes; Serves: 6

Ingredients:

- 1½ tsp. of black pepper (freshly ground)

- 1½ tsp. of salt

- 2¼ lb. (680 g) of whole fresh sardines (remove the scales)

- 3 cups of flour

- Avocado oil (as required)

Instructions:

1.   Place the skillet to preheat over medium heat. Pour in as much oil that will fill approximately an inch of the pan.

2.   Use pepper and salt to season the fish.

3.   Completely dip the fish inside the flour.

4.   Place 1 fish in the pan at a time but do not overcrowd it.

5.   Let it cook on each side for 3 minutes until both sides of the fish are brown.

6.   Serve while it's still hot.

Nutritional Information:

Calories: 794; Carbohydrates: 44g; Fat: 47g; Fiber: 2g; Protein: 48g

ITALIAN FRIED SHRIMP

Preparation time: 10 minutes; Cooking time: 5 minutes; Serves: 6

Ingredients:

- 1½ cup of flour

- 1½ lb. (454 g) of 21 to 25 large shrimp (peeled and deveined)

- 1½ tsp. of salt

- 3 cups of Italian bread crumbs (seasoned)

- 3 large eggs

- Extra-virgin olive oil

Instructions:

1. Beat the eggs inside a small bowl with 1 tbsp. of water and pour it into a deep plate.

2. Mix the breadcrumbs with salt on a different deep plate.

3. Get a third deep plate and put the flour in it.

4. Fully immerse the prawns inside the flour first, then in the egg mixture, before dipping it in the breadcrumbs. Place it on a flat plate and do the same with the remaining prawns.

5. Pour enough olive oil into a skillet placed over high heat. Place the shrimps in the hot oil and cook both sides for 2 – 3 minutes.

6. Take out the prawns from the pan and place them on an absorbent paper to drain.

7.   Serve while it's still hot.

Nutritional Information:

Calories: 714; Carbohydrates: 63g; Fat: 34g; Fiber: 3g; Protein: 37g

SHRIMP WITH GARLIC AND MUSHROOMS

Preparation time: 10 minutes; Cooking time: 15 minutes; Serves: 6

Ingredients:

- ¾ tsp. of red pepper flakes

- 1/3 cup of fresh flat-leaf Italian parsley (chopped)

- 1½ cup of extra-virgin olive oil

- 1½ lb. (454 g) of fresh shrimp (peeled and deveined)

- 1½ tsp. of salt

- 6 oz. (113 g) of sliced mushrooms (baby Bella, shiitake, or button)

- 12 large, thinly sliced garlic cloves

- For serving: Riced cauliflower or zucchini noodles

Instructions:

1.   Rinse and dry the shrimp. Then place them in a little bowl and sprinkle them properly with salt.

2.   Set a large skillet with thick sides on medium-low heat and pour the olive oil into it. As it heats, add the garlic and leave for about 3 to 4 minutes to get fragrant. Reduce the heat once the garlic starts burning.

3.   Sauté the mushrooms in the skillet for 5 minutes. When it gets soft, add the chili flakes and shrimp then sauté for additional 3-4 minutes until the shrimp begin to turn pink.

4.   Take it off the heat and add the parsley. Stir properly.

5.   Serve on cauliflower rice or courgette noodles.

Nutritional Information:

Calories: 620; Carbohydrates: 4 g; Fat: 56 g; Fiber: 0 g; Protein: 24 g; Sodium: 736 mg

THYME WHOLE ROASTED RED SNAPPER

Preparation time: 5 minutes; Cooking time: 45 minutes; Serves: 6

Ingredients:

- 6 or 5 thyme sprigs

- 4½ sliced garlic cloves

- 1½ (2 to 2½ lb. or 907 g to 1.1 kg) of whole red snapper (cleaned and scaled)

- 3 sliced lemons (about 10 slices)

- 4½ tbsps. of cold salted butter (divided and cut into small cubes) (optional)

Instructions:

1. Let the oven preheat to 350°F (180°C or Fan 160°C).

2. Cut an aluminum foil piece to fit into your pan, then place the foil on top of the baking sheet.

3. Slice horizontally across the fish's belly to make a pocket.

4. Place 3 slices of lemon on the aluminum foil then place the fish on the lemons.

5. Stuff garlic, 3 slices of lemon, butter, and thyme into the fish. Reserve 3 butter pieces.

6. Keep the 3 remaining pieces of butter on the fish and top with 3 – 4 slices of lemon. Seal the foil to create a pocket around the fish.

7.   Put the fish inside the oven and let it cook for up to 45 minutes.

8.   Serve alongside the other fresh slices of lemon.

Nutritional Information:

Calories: 345; Carbohydrates: 12 g; Fat: 13 g; Fiber: 3 g; Protein: 54 g; Sodium: 170 mg

POULTRY

GREEK CHICKEN RICE

Preparation time: 10 minutes; Cooking time: 14 minutes; Serves: 6

Ingredients:

- 1/3 cup of fresh parsley (chopped)
- 1½ zucchini (cut into slices)
- 1½ cup of rice (rinsed and drained)
- 1½ tbsps. of oregano
- 1½ tbsps. of minced garlic
- 1½ diced onion
- 2¼ cups of chicken broth
- 3 chopped peppers
- 4½ chicken breasts (skinless, boned, & cut into pieces)
- 4½ tbsps. of fresh lemon juice
- 4½ tbsps. of olive oil

Instructions:

1. Pour oil into the Instant Pot's inner pot and set it on sauté mode.

2. Throw in the chicken and onion then cook for up to 5 minutes.

3. Add the oregano, rice, garlic, lemon juice, pepper, broth, and salt. Mix properly.

4. Seal with the lid and let it cook for 4 minutes on high heat.

5. Afterwards, do a quick release of the pressure and take off the lid.

6. Add the zucchini, peppers, and parsley. Mix properly.

7. Use the lid to seal the pot, select manual, and set the timer to 5 minutes.

8. Do a quick release of the pressure and take off the cover.

9. Mix properly, serve, and enjoy.

Nutritional Information:

Calories: 500; Carbohydrates: 48 g; Fat: 16 g; Fiber: 3 g; Protein: 38 g; Sodium: 573 mg

CHICKEN AND OLIVES
Preparation time: 10 minutes; Cooking time: 15 minutes; Serves: 6

Ingredients:

*   ¾ cup of chicken stock

*   1/3 cup green olives (pitted & sliced)

*   1½ cup of chopped red onion

*   1½ tbsps. of dried oregano

*   2¼ cups of cubed tomatoes

*   3 tbsps. of minced garlic

*   3 tbsps. of olive oil

*   6 chicken breasts (skinless & boneless)

*   A handful of parsley (chopped)

*   Black pepper (to taste)

*   Juice of a lemon

*   Salt (to taste)

Instructions:

1.   Heat the oil in a pan over medium-high heat. Add the chicken, salt, garlic, and pepper to the pot and sauté each side for 2 minutes.

2.   Add the remaining ingredients and mix thoroughly. Let it boil then cook for 13 minutes over medium heat.

3.   Divide and serve on different plates.

Nutritional Information:

Calories: 135; Carbohydrates: 12 g; Fat: 5 g; Fiber: 3 g; Protein: 9 g; Sodium: 573 mg

MOROCCAN CHICKEN THIGHS AND VEGETABLE TAGINE
Preparation time: 15 minutes; Cooking time: 52 minutes; Serves: 4

Ingredients:

- 1/3 cup of extra-virgin olive oil (divided)

- 1/3 tsp. of black pepper (freshly ground)

- 1/8 cup of fresh cilantro (chopped) or flat-leaf Italian parsley

- 2/3 cup of pitted halved olives (Kalamata or Spanish green work nicely)

- 2/3 cup of water

- 2/3 red bell pepper (cut into 1" squares)

- 2/3 small red onion (chopped)

- 1 lb. (680 g) boneless skinless chicken thighs (cut into 1" chunks)

- 1 tsp. of salt (divided)

- 11/3 medium tomatoes (chopped or 1½ cups of diced canned tomatoes)

- 11/3 medium zucchini (sliced into ¼" thick half-moons)

- For serving: Sautéed spinach or riced cauliflower

Instructions:

1.   Get a skillet with large sides or a Dutch oven, set it on medium-high heat, and pour ¼ cup of olive into it to heat.

2.   Use 1 tsp. of pepper and salt to season, the chicken then sautésé for 6 – 8 minutes until all the sides are golden brown.

3.   Add the peppers and onions then sauté for another 6 to 8 minutes until wilted.

4.   Add the water and chopped tomatoes, let it boil, then reduce to low heat. Cover and allow to simmer for 30-45 minutes until the meat is tender and well cooked.

5.   Stir in the zucchini, leftover ¼ cup of olive oil, cilantro, and olives. Let it cook uncovered, over low heat for about 10 minutes until the courgettes get tender.

6.   Serve hot on sautéed spinach or with cauliflower rice.

Nutritional Information:

Calories: 358; Carbohydrates: 8 g; Fat: 24 g; Fiber: 3 g; Protein: 25 g; Sodium: 977 mg

YOGURT-MARINATED CHICKEN

Preparation time: 15 minutes; Cooking time: 30 minutes; Serves: 4

Not great

Ingredients:

- 1 cup of plain Greek yogurt
- 1 tsp. of salt
- 2 tbsps. of olive oil
- 4 (4 oz. or 113 g) of skinless, boneless chicken breasts
- 4 tbsps. of minced fresh oregano (or 1 tbsp. of dried oregano)
- 6 minced garlic cloves
- Zest of 1 lemon

Instructions:

1. Put the yogurt, oregano, garlic, olive oil, lemon zest, and salt inside a medium bowl and stir to mix. Add a little lemon juice or a few tbsps. of water to dilute if the yogurt is too thick.

2. Add the chicken and coat it very well inside the marinade. Cover the chicken and place it in the fridge overnight or for 30 minutes at least.

3. Let the oven preheat to 350ºF (180ºC). Keep the rack in the center.

4. Roast the chicken on a roasting pan for 30 minutes or until it reaches 165ºF (74ºC).

Nutritional Information:

Calories: 255; Carbohydrates: 8 g; Fat: 13 g; Fiber: 2 g; Protein: 29 g; Sodium: 694 mg

TRADITIONAL CHICKEN SHAWARMA

Preparation time: 15 minutes; Cooking time: 15 minutes; Serves: 6

Ingredients:

- ¾ cup of extra-virgin olive oil
- ¾ cup of lemon juice
- ¾ tsp. of cinnamon
- ¾ tsp. of freshly ground black pepper
- ¾ tsp. of ground cardamom
- 2¼ tsps. of salt
- 3 lb. (907 g) of skinless and boneless chicken
- 4½ tbsps. of minced garlic
- For serving: Hummus and pita bread (optional)

Instructions:

1.   Cut the skinless and boneless chicken into 1-inch skinless and boneless strips inside a big bowl.

2.   Get a different bowl and whisk the lemon juice, garlic, olive oil, cinnamon, cardamom, pepper, and salt together in it.

3.   Coat the dressing over all the chicken.

4.   Allow the chicken to rest for approximately 10 minutes.

5.   Heat a big skillet on medium-high heat then cook the pieces of chicken for 12 minutes, while using the tongs to turn the chicken from time to time.

6.   Serve alongside the pita bread and hummus, if you please.

Nutritional Information:

Calories: 477; Carbohydrates: 5 g; Fat: 32 g; Fiber: 1 g; Protein: 47 g; Sodium: 1234 mg

LEMON-GARLIC WHOLE CHICKEN AND POTATOES
Preparation time: 10 minutes; Cooking time: 45 minutes; Serves: 6

Ingredients:

- 1½ cup of minced garlic

- 1½ cup of plus 2 tbsps. extra-virgin olive oil (divided)

- 1½ tsp. of black pepper (freshly ground)

- 1½ whole chicken (cut into 8 pieces)

- 1½ lb. (454 g) red potatoes or fingerling

- 2¼ cups of lemon juice

- 2¼ tsp. of salt (divided)

Instructions:

1. Let the oven preheat to 400°F (200°C or Fan 180°C).

2. Whisk the lemon juice, garlic, and 1 tsp. of salt, 1 cup of olive oil, and pepper together in a big bowl.

3. Put the chicken inside a big roasting pan then cover the chicken with half of the lemon sauce. Use the foil to cover the pan then let it bake for 20 minutes.

4. Cut the potatoes into two halves and use 1 tsp. of salt and 2 tbsps. of olive oil to season it. Put them on top of a baking sheet and let it bake inside the same oven the chicken is in for 20 minutes.

5. Remove the chicken and potatoes from the oven. Use a spatula to move the potatoes to join the chicken in the pan. Pour the leftover sauce on the chicken and potatoes and allow to bake for extra 25 minutes.

6.   Place the potatoes and chicken on a serving dish then pour the lemon sauce and garlic over them.

Nutritional Information:

Calories: 959; Carbohydrates: 37 g; Fat: 78 g; Fiber: 4 g; Protein: 33 g; Sodium: 1005 mg

GREEK LEMON CHICKEN KEBABS

Preparation time: 15 minutes; Cooking time: 20 minutes; Serves: 4

Ingredients:

- 1 cup of extra-virgin olive oil (divided)

- 1 large lemon (juiced)

- 1 tsp. of za'atar seasoning

- 2 large red bell pepper (cut into 1 ¼ inch pieces)

- 2 lb. (454 g) boneless, skinless chicken breasts (cut into 1¼ inch cubes)

- 4 garlic cloves (minced)

- 4 large shallots (diced into quarters)

- 4 small-sized zucchini (nearly 1 lb. or 454 g) (cut into rounds a little under ½ inch thick)

- Black pepper (Freshly ground) (to taste)

- Salt (to taste)

- Tzatziki sauce (for serving)

Instructions:

1.   Whisk the lemon juice, $^1/_3$ cup olive oil, za'atar, garlic, pepper, and salt.

2.   Put the chicken inside a medium bowl then pour the mixture of olive oil over it. Press it into the marinade, then cover and keep in the fridge for 45 minutes. While marinating the chicken, let the wooden skewers soak in water for about 30 minutes.

3.   Season the pepper, shallots, courgettes, and the remaining 2½ tbsps. of olive oil. Lightly season with salt.

4.   Let the oven preheat to 500ºF (260ºC) and place a pan over it to heat.

5.   Slip the courgette, red pepper, 2 chicken pieces, and scallion on each of the skewers and repeat the process twice. Put the skewers on top of the hot pan so it cooks for 7 to 9 minutes or just until the chicken is properly cooked. Halfway through, turn it once then serve hot alongside the tzatziki sauce.

6.   Enjoy.

Nutritional Information:

Calories: 825; Carbohydrates: 31 g; Fat: 59 g; Fiber: 5 g; Protein: 51 g; Sodium: 379 mg

CHICKEN SHISH TAWOOK

Preparation time: 15 minutes; Cooking time: 15 minutes; Serves: 6

Ingredients:

- ¾ cup of extra-virgin olive oil

- ¾ cup of lemon juice

- ¾ tsp. of black pepper (freshly ground)

- 1 ½ tsps. of smoked paprika

- 2 ¼ tsps. of salt

- 3 lb. (907 g) of boneless & skinless chicken (thighs or breasts)

- 3 tbsps. of minced garlic

- 3 tbsps. of tomato paste

- For serving: Tzatziki, rice, or hummus (optional)

Instructions:

1. Put the garlic, paprika, tomato paste, olive oil, lemon juice, pepper, and salt together in a big bowl then whisk to mix.

2. Chop the chicken into ½-inch cubes and put them inside the big bowl. Combine to coat properly with the marinade then side it aside for 10 minutes, at least.

3. Make the grill preheat on high. Put the chicken over the skewers then cook each side for 3 minutes; that's 9 minutes in total.

4. Pan-fry by preheating the pan on high heat. Add the chicken, and while using tongs to turn them, cook them for 9 minutes.

5.   Serve the chicken alongside rice, hummus, or tzatziki as desired.

6.   Enjoy.

Nutritional Information:

Calories: 482; Carbohydrates: 6 g; Fat: 32 g; Fiber: 1 g; Protein: 47 g; Sodium: 1298 mg

CHICKEN MEATBALLS WITH PARMESAN

Preparation time: 0 minutes; Cooking time: 20 minutes; Serves: 8

Ingredients:

For the Meatballs:

- ½ tsp. of dried basil
- 2/3 tsp. of cayenne pepper
- 1 cup of grated Parmesan cheese
- 11/3 tbsps. of chopped sage leaves
- 11/3 tsp. of shallot powder
- 12/3 lbs. of ground chicken
- 22/3 tsps. of porcini powder
- 22/3 finely minced garlic cloves
- 22/3 lightly beaten eggs
- Ground black pepper
- Salt

For the sauce:

- 2/3 tbsp. of lard at room temperature
- 11/3 cup of chicken consommé
- 11/3 peeled & finely chopped onion
- 2 2/3 pureed tomatoes

Instructions:

1.   Mix all the ingredients for the meatballs together inside a mixing ball. Roll it into bite-sized balls.

2.   Melt 1 tbsp. of lard over moderately high heat inside a skillet. Sear the meatballs until they are properly cooked after about 3 minutes. Reserve.

3.   Melt the leftover lard then let the onions cook until they are translucent and tender. Add the chicken consommé and pureed tomatoes then cook for additional 4 minutes.

4.   Add the reserved meatballs, put the heat on simmer, and let it continue cooking for 6-7 minutes.

To Store:

1.   Get Ziploc bags or airtight containers and put the meatballs in them then refrigerate for 3-4 days.

2.   Refrigerate the heavy-duty freezer bags or airtight containers and freeze for 3 to 4 months. Reheat slowly inside a saucepan to defrost.

3.   Enjoy.

Nutritional Information:

Calories: 252; Carbohydrates: 5.3g; Fat: 9.7g; Fiber: 1.4g; Protein: 34.2g; Sodium: 0mg

MOROCCAN CHICKEN MEATBALLS

Preparation time: 10 minutes; Cooking time: 10 minutes; Serves: 6

Ingredients:

- ¼ tsp. of ground cardamom
- ¾ tsp. of black pepper (freshly ground)
- ¾ cup of all-purpose flour (to coat)
- ¾ tsp. of garlic powder
- ¾ tsp. of ground coriander
- ¾ tsp. of salt
- 1/3 cup of olive oil (divided)
- 1½ lb. (454 g) of ground chicken
- 1½ tsp. of ground cumin
- 3 large, diced shallots
- 3 tbsps. of parsley (finely chopped)
- 3 tsps. of paprika

Instructions:

1.   Mix the paprika, shallot, garlic powder, parsley, coriander, cumin, cardamom, salt, and pepper.

2.   Put the chicken inside the spice mixture. Mix properly and roll into flattened 1-inch balls about ½ inch thick.

3.   Put the flour inside a dredging bowl and completely cover the balls inside the flour.

4.   Heat enough oil inside a skillet or pan and let it heat on medium heat. Batch by batch, cook each side of the meatballs through for 2 to 3 minutes, turning often. If required between batches, add more oil. Serve inside a pita and top with lettuce and creamy yogurt sauce.

5.   Enjoy.

Nutritional Information:

Calories: 405; Carbohydrates: 20 g; Fat: 26 g; Fiber: 1 g; Protein: 24 g; Sodium: 387 mg

POACHED CHICKEN BREAST WITH ROMESCO SAUCE

Preparation time: 10 minutes; Cooking time: 12 minutes; Serves: 4

Ingredients:

- 1/3 halved onion

- 1/8 tsp. of black pepper (freshly ground)

- 2/3 carrot (halved)

- 2/3 celery stalk (halved)

- 2/3 cup of romesco sauce

- 1 lb. (680 g) of chicken breasts (boneless, skinless, & cut into 6 pieces)

- 11/3 smashed garlic cloves

- 11/3 tbsps. of chopped fresh flat-leaf (Italian) parsley

- 2 sprigs of rosemary or fresh thyme

Instructions:

1.   Put the chicken inside a medium-sized saucepan. Fill it up with water until about an inch covers the chicken. Add the celery, carrot, thyme, onion, and garlic then cover and allow it to boil. Then reduce to low heat and allow it to cook for 12 to 15 minutes or just until the chicken's core temperature reaches 74ºC (165ºF) on the meat thermometer and its juices are all out.

2.   Take the chicken out of the water and allow it to rest for about 5 minutes.

3.   When the chicken is ready to be served, apply   ¾ cup of the romesco sauce to a serving dish's bottom. Place the chicken breasts on it and use the leftover romesco sauce to drizzle the top. Sprinkle pepper and parsley on the surface.

4. Enjoy.

Nutritional Information:

Calories: 270; Carbohydrates: 31 g; Fat: 10 g; Fiber: 2 g; Protein: 13 g; Sodium: 647 mg

PEACH-GLAZED CHICKEN DRUMSTICKS

Preparation time: 10 minutes; Cooking time: 20 minutes; Serves: 6

Ingredients:

- ¾ tsp. of smoked paprika

- 1/3 cup of cider vinegar

- 1/3 cup of honey

- 1/3 tsp. of black pepper (freshly ground)

- 1/3 tsp. of sea salt or kosher

- 1½ (15 oz. or 425 g) can of sliced peaches in 100 percent juice (drained)

- 4½ garlic cloves

- 12 chicken drumsticks (2 lb. or 907 g) (skin removed)

- Nonstick cooking spray

Instructions:

1.   Take the chicken out of the freezer.

2.   Set the oven rack approximately 4 inches beneath the grill element. Let the oven preheat to 500ºF (260ºC). Use aluminum foil to line a big, rimmed baking sheet. Cover the aluminum foil with a wire cooling grid and use non-stick cooking spray to spray the grid. Set aside.

3.   Mix the honey, peaches, garlic, vinegar, smoked paprika, pepper, and salt inside a blender. Blend until smooth.

4.   Put the puree in the medium saucepan then set to boil on medium-high heat. Stirring continually, cook it for 2 minutes and divide into 2

bowls. While you will brush the 1st bowl on the chicken, set the 2nd bowl aside to serve.

5.   Use about ½ the sauce to brush all the chicken sides and reserve the remaining ½ for the 2nd layer of coating. Put the thighs on top of the grill you prepared and let it roast for about 10 minutes.

6.   Take the chicken out of the oven, setting the rack on a high. Use the leftover sauce to brush the chicken. Put the chicken back into the oven and leave to cook for up to 5 minutes. Turn it over and cook for an additional 3 to 5 minutes until its juices are clear or a meat thermometer shows that its core temperature has reached 74ºC (165ºF). Serve alongside the sauce you reserved.

7.   Enjoy.

Nutritional Information:

Calories: 526; Carbohydrates: 38 g; Fat: 22 g; Fiber: 1 g; Protein: 44 g; Sodium: 412 mg

BEEF, PORK, & LAMB
TURKEY BACON BITES
Preparation time: 0 minutes; Cooking time: 5 minutes; Serves: 6

Ingredients:

- 1½ deveined and minced jalapeno pepper

- 1½ tbsps. of cold butter

- 1½ tsp. of Mexican oregano

- 3 tbsps. of finely chopped scallions

- 6 oz. of chopped turkey bacon

- 6 oz. of Neufchatel cheese

Instructions:

1.   Mix all the ingredients inside a mixing bowl.

2.   Roll into 8 balls.

To Store:

1.   Divide the bites of turkey bacon among two Ziploc bags or airtight containers. Refrigerate for 3 - 5 days.

2.   Enjoy.

Nutritional Information:

Calories: 190; Carbohydrates: 2.2g; Fat: 16.7g; Fiber: 0.3g; Protein: 8.8g; Sodium: 0mg

GRILLED BEEF KEBABS

Preparation time: 15 minutes; Cooking time: 10 minutes; Serves: 4

Ingredients:

- $^1/_3$ cup of extra-virgin olive oil
- $^1/_3$ tsp. of ground allspice
- $^1/_3$ tsp. of ground nutmeg
- 2/3 large onion (chop them into 8 quarters)
- 2/3 large red bell pepper (chop them into 1-inch cubes)
- 2/3 tsp. of black pepper (freshly ground)
- 1 tsp. of salt
- $1^1/_3$ lb. (907 g) of beef fillet

Instructions:

1.   Set a lightly-oiled skillet, grill, or grill pan to preheat to high heat.

2.   Chop the beef into 1" cubes and place them inside a big bowl.

3.   Combine the salt, allspice, nutmeg, and black pepper inside a small bowl.

4.   Pour olive oil on the beef them toss it to coat properly. Sprinkle seasoning evenly over the beef and toss until all the pieces are coated.

5.   Skewer with bell pepper or onion piece, alternating them every minute or 2.

6.   To cook it, keep the skewers on top of the skillet or grill, turning every 2-3 minutes to cook all the sides properly; for medium-rare, 6 minutes and for well done, 8 minutes.

7.   Serve while it's still warm.

Nutritional Information:

Calories: 485; Carbohydrates: 4 g; Fat: 36 g; Fiber: 1 g; Protein: 35 g; Sodium: 1453 mg

PORK WRAPS

Preparation time: 0 minutes; Cooking time: 15 minutes; Serves: 6

Ingredients:

- 1½ deveined & finely minced chili pepper
- 1½ head lettuce
- 1½ lb. of ground pork
- 1½ tbsps. of champagne vinegar
- 1½ tbsps. of coconut aminos
- 1½ tsp. of mustard powder
- 2¼ tbsps. of sunflower seeds
- 3 finely minced garlic cloves
- 3 sliced scallion stalks
- Celery salt & ground black pepper (to taste)

Instructions:

1. Place the ground pork inside a preheated pan to sear for approximately 8 minutes at 350oF. Add the chili pepper, garlic, sunflower seeds, and mustard seeds and stir. Keep sautéing until after a minute when it gets aromatic.

2. Stir in the coconut aminos, vinegar, scallions, black pepper, and salt.

To Store:

1. Put the mixture of ground pork inside Ziploc bags or airtight containers and refrigerate for at least 3 days.

2. To freeze, place the mixture of ground pork inside heavy-duty freezer bags or airtight containers and keep it in the freezer for 2 to 3

months. Keep inside the refrigerator to defrost then place in a skillet to reheat.

3.   Scoop spoonfuls of the pork mixture on the lettuce leaves, wrap, and serve.

Nutritional Information:

Calories: 281; Carbohydrates: 5.1 g; Fat: 19.4 g; Fiber: 1.3 g; Protein: 22.1 g; Sodium: 0 mg

MEDITERRANEAN LAMB BOWLS

Preparation time: 15 minutes; Cooking time: 15 minutes; Serves: 4

Ingredients:

- ½ cup of yellow onion (diced)

- ½ tsp. of garlic powder

- 1 cup of cherry tomatoes (halved)

- 1 tsp. of red pepper flakes

- 1 tsp. of za'atar seasoning

- 2 cups of cooked rice

- 2 cups of crumbled feta cheese

- 2 cups of store-bought hummus

- 2 lb. (454 g) of ground lamb

- 2 peeled and diced cucumbers

- 2 tsps. of dried mint

- 2 tsps. of dried parsley

- 4 tbsps. of extra-virgin olive oil

- 4 warmed pita bread (optional)

Instructions:

1. Heat olive oil inside a large skillet or sauté pan over medium heat then let the onion cook for approximately 2 minutes until fragrant.

2. Place the lamb inside and mix while you break it up as it cooks.

3. After cooking the lamb halfway, add parsley, mint, garlic powder, and red pepper flakes.

4.   Mix the cooked rice with the za'atar inside a medium bowl, then share between separate serving bowls. Add the lamb you seasoned then top with the cucumber, tomatoes, feta, hummus, and pita (if you're using it).

5.   Serve.

Nutritional Information:

Calories: 1312; Carbohydrates: 62 g; Fat: 96 g; Fiber: 12 g; Protein: 62 g; Sodium: 1454 mg

BEEF KOFTA

Preparation time: 10 minutes; Cooking time: 5 minutes; Serves: 6

Ingredients:

- ¾ tsp. of black pepper (freshly ground)
- 1/3 cup of fresh Italian parsley
- 1/3 tsp. of cinnamon
- 1/3 tsp. of ground cumin
- 1½ lb. (454 g) ground beef
- 1½ medium onion
- 1½ tsp. of salt

Instructions:

1. Let a grill or grill pan preheat to high.

2. Mince the parsley and onion inside a food processor till finely chopped.

3. Use your hands to mix the ground cumin, onion mix, pepper, cinnamon, and salt inside a large bowl.

4. Share the meat in 6 portions.

5. Form a flat oval out of each portion.

6. Put the patties on top of the grill pan or grill then let each side cook for about 3 minutes.

7. Serve and enjoy.

Nutritional Information:

Calories: 203; Carbohydrates: 3 g; Fat: 10 g; Fiber: 1 g; Protein: 24 g; Sodium: 655 mg

CHICKEN MEATBALLS WITH PARMESAN

Preparation time: 0 minutes; Cooking time: 20 minutes; Serves: 8

Ingredients:

For the Meatballs:

- ½ tsp. of dried basil
- 1 cup of grated Parmesan cheese
- 11/3 tbsps. of chopped sage leaves
- 11/3 tsp. of shallot powder
- 12/3 pounds of ground chicken
- 2/3 tsp. of cayenne pepper
- 22/3 finely minced garlic cloves
- 22/3 lightly beaten eggs
- 22/3 tsp. of porcini powder
- Ground black pepper
- Salt

For the sauce:

- 2/3 tbsps. of lard (room temperature)
- 11/3 cup of chicken consommé
- 11/3 onion (peeled & finely chopped)
- 22/3 pureed tomatoes

Instructions:

1.   Mix all the ingredients for the meatballs together inside a mixing bowl and roll into bite-sized balls.

2.	Melt a tbsp. of lard inside a skillet on medium-high heat. Let the meatballs seat for approximately 3 minutes until it cooks thoroughly. Reserve.

3.	Melt the leftover lard then let the onion cook until it becomes translucent and tender. Add the chicken consommé and pureed tomatoes and keep cooking for additional 4 minutes.

4.	Add the meatballs you preserved, set the heat on simmer, and continue cooking for 6-7 minutes.

To Store:

1.	Put the meatballs inside Ziploc bags or airtight containers then refrigerate them for 3 – 4 days.

2.	Leave the meatballs to freeze for 3 to 4 months inside heavy-duty freezer bags or airtight containers. Reheat in a saucepan slowly to defrost.

3.	Enjoy.

Nutritional Information:

Calories: 252; Carbohydrates: 5.3 g; Fat: 9.7 g; Fiber: 1.4 g; Protein: 34.2 g; Sodium: 0 mg

MOROCCAN CHICKEN MEATBALLS
Preparation time: 10 minutes; Cooking time: 10 minutes; Serves: 6

Ingredients:

- ¼ tsp. of ground cardamom
- ¾ cup of all-purpose flour (to coat)
- ¾ tsp. of black pepper (freshly ground)
- ¾ tsp. of garlic powder
- ¾ tsp. of ground coriander
- ¾ tsp. of salt
- 1/3 cup of olive oil (divided)
- 1½ tsp. of ground cumin
- 1½ lb. (454 g) of ground chicken
- 3 large shallots (diced)
- 3 tbsps. of parsley (finely chopped)
- 3 tsp. of paprika

Instructions:

1. Mix the parsley, shallot, paprika, coriander, cumin, cardamom, parsley, pepper, and salt inside a bowl.

2. Put the chicken inside the spice mixture, mix properly, then flatten to about half an inch thick and roll into 1-inch balls.

3. Place the flour inside a dredging bowl and cover the rolled balls in the flour.

4.   Pour enough oil into the bottom of a skillet or pan and let it heat on medium heat. Cook the meatballs in batches turning often and cooking each side for 2-3 minutes until properly cooked. Between batches, add more oil as required. Serve topped with lettuce and then creamy yogurt sauce in a pita.

5.   Enjoy.

Nutritional Information:

Calories: 405; Carbohydrates: 20 g; Fat: 26 g; Fiber: 1 g; Protein: 24 g; Sodium: 387 mg

PARSLEY-DIJON CHICKEN AND POTATOES

Preparation time: 10 minutes; Cooking time: 22 minutes; Serves: 4

Ingredients:

- 1/8 cup of dry white wine

- 1/8 tsp. of black pepper (freshly ground)

- 1/8 tsp. of kosher or sea salt

- 2/3 cup of flat-leaf (Italian) parsley (chopped fresh, including stems)

- 2/3 cup of no-salt-added or low-sodium chicken broth

- 2/3 tbsp. of Dijon mustard

- 2/3 tbsp. of extra-virgin olive oil

- 2/3 tbsp. of lemon juice (freshly squeezed)

- 1 lb. (680 g) of chicken thighs (boneless and skinless, cut into 1-inch cubes and patted dry)

- 1 lb. (680 g) of Yukon Gold potatoes (unpeeled and cut into ½-inch cubes)

- 11/3 minced garlic cloves

Instructions:

1.   Heat the oil inside a large skillet placed over medium-high heat. Put the chicken in the oil to cook for about 5 minutes, turning the chicken over when one side is browned. Take out the chicken and keep it on a plate.

2.   Cook potatoes in a pan for 5 minutes and stir when one side of the potatoes turns golden and crisp. Put the potatoes to the pan's side and stir in the garlic and cook for a minute. Pour in the wine and let it cook for a minute until it almost evaporates. Add the mustard, chicken stock, pepper, salt, and reserved chicken. Increase the heat to high heat and let it boil.

3.	When it begins to boil, cover it and lower to medium-low heat, and cook for about 10 to 12 minutes until the chicken's core temperature reaches 74ºC (165ºF) on a meat thermometer, juices are not coming out, or the potatoes get tender.

4.	Stir the parsley in at the last meeting of the cooking and take off from the heat. Add lemon juice, then serve.

Nutritional Information:

Calories: 324; Carbohydrates: 45 g; Fat: 9 g; Fiber: 5 g; Protein: 16 g; Sodium: 560 mg

POACHED CHICKEN BREAST WITH ROMESCO SAUCE

Preparation time: 10 minutes; Cooking time: 22 minutes; Serves: 4

Ingredients:

- 1/3 halved onion
- 1/8 tsp. of freshly ground black pepper
- 2/3 carrot, halved
- 2/3 celery stalk, halved
- 2/3 cup of romesco sauce
- 1 lb. (680 g) of boneless & skinless chicken breasts (cut into 6 pieces)
- 11/3 smashed garlic cloves
- 11/3 tbsps. of chopped fresh flat-leaf (Italian) parsley
- 2 sprigs of fresh thyme (or rosemary)

Instructions:

1. Put the chicken inside a medium saucepan and fill it up with enough water to leave at least 1 inch of chicken above the chicken. Throw in the carrot, thyme, celery, garlic, and onion then cover and let it boil. Lower to low heat and allow it to cook for 12 to 15 minutes, or till the chicken's core temperature on a meat thermometer gets to 74ºC (165ºF) and all its juices are out.

2. Get the chicken out of the water and allow it to rest for about 5 minutes.

3. Spread ¾ of the cup of romesco sauce on a serving dish's bottom whenever you are ready to serve. Top up with the chicken breasts and use the leftover romesco sauce to drizzle. Then sprinkle pepper and parsley on the surface and enjoy.

Nutritional Information:

Calories: 270; Carbohydrates: 31 g; Fat: 10 g; Fiber: 2 g; Protein: 13 g; Sodium: 647 mg

PEACH-GLAZED CHICKEN DRUMSTICKS

Preparation time: 10 minutes; Cooking time: 20 minutes; Serves: 6

Ingredients:

- ¾ tsp. of smoked paprika

- 1/3 cup of cider vinegar

- 1/3 cup of honey

- 1/3 tsp. of black pepper (freshly ground)

- 1/3 tsp. of kosher or sea salt

- 1½ (15 oz. or 425 g) can of sliced peaches in 100% juice (drained)

- 4½ garlic cloves

- 12 chicken drumsticks (2 lb or 907 g) (remove the skin)

- Nonstick cooking spray

Instructions:

1. Get the chicken out of the fridge.

2. Put the oven rack approximately 4 inches under the grill element. Let the oven preheat to 500ºF (260ºC). Use aluminum foil to line a big, rimmed baking sheet. Then keep a wire cooling grid atop the aluminum foil, spray with non-stick cooking spray, and set aside.

3. Put the peaches, vinegar, smoked paprika, honey, pepper, garlic, and salt together in a blender and blend until smooth.

4. Pour the puree into a medium saucepan set on medium-high heat and allow to boil. Stir while it cooks for 2 minutes. Share the sauce into 2 separate bowls. Brush the first bowl on the chicken and set the 2nd bowl aside for serving.

5.   Use approximately half the sauce to brush all the chicken's sides and reserve the remaining half for the 2nd coating. Keep the thighs on top of the peppered grill to roast for about 10 minutes.

6.   Get the chicken out of the oven and let the rack be on high. Use the leftover sauce in the 1st bowl to brush the chicken then return it to the oven and let it cook there for 5 minutes. Flip the chicken over and cook for an additional 3 to 5 minutes until the juices are clear and its core temperature gets to 74ºC (165ºF) on the meat thermometer.

7.   Serve alongside the sauce you reserved.

Nutritional Information:

Calories: 526; Carbohydrates: 38 g; Fat: 22 g; Fiber: 1 g; Protein: 44 g; Sodium: 412 mg

VEGETABLES

SAUTÉED CABBAGE

Preparation time: 10 minutes; Cooking time: 15 minutes; Serves: 6

Ingredients:

- 1/3 cup of chopped fresh parsley

- 1/3 tsp. of black pepper

- 1½ onion (halved & sliced thin)

- 1½ small head of green cabbage cored & sliced thin (about 1¼ lb. or 567 g)

- 11/8 tsp. of salt (divided)

- 2¼ tsps. of lemon juice

- 3 tbsps. of extra-virgin olive oil (divided)

Instructions:

1.   Pour cold water into a big bowl and add the cabbage then allow it to sit for up to 3 minutes. Drain properly.

2.   Put a tbsp. of oil inside a skillet, allow it to heat on medium-high heat till it shimmers. Add a quarter tsp. of the salt and the onion then cook until it softens or browns lightly in 5-7 minutes. Move to a bowl.

3.   Put the leftover 1 tbsp. of oil to heat inside the empty skillet placed on medium-high heat and let it shimmer. Put the cabbage into the skillet and use half a tsp. of black pepper and salt to sprinkle it. Cover it and cook without stirring for approximately 3 minutes until the cabbage wilts or browns lightly on the bottom.

4.   Stir properly and keep cooking uncovered for approximately 4 minutes until the cabbage becomes crispy and tender, and some parts turn lightly brown. Flip once halfway through and turn off the heat. Add the cooked onion, lemon juice, and parsley and stir.

5.   Move to a plate, serve, and enjoy.

Nutritional Information:

Calories: 117; Carbohydrates: 13 g; Fat: 7 g; Fiber: 5 g; Protein: 3 g; Sodium: 472 mg

CRISPY ARTICHOKES WITH LEMON

Preparation time: 10 minutes; Cooking time: 15 minutes; Serves: 4

Ingredients:

- ½ cup of whole wheat bread crumbs

- ½ tsp. of paprika

- ½ tsp. of salt

- 1 lemon

- 2 (15 oz. or 425 g) cans of artichoke hearts in water (drained)

- 2 eggs

- 2 tbsps. of water

Instructions:

1.   Let the air fryer preheat to 380ºF (193ºC).

2.   Put the egg inside a medium-low bowl, add water and beat until frothy.

3.   Get a different medium-deep bowl then combine the breadcrumbs, paprika, and salt in it.

4.   First dip each of the artichoke hearts inside the egg mixture, then dip it inside the breadcrumb mixture, and then cover it with crumbs. Place the artichoke hearts inside the air fryer basket in a single layer.

5.   Let the artichoke hearts fry for 15 minutes.

6.   Get the artichokes out of the deep fryer, squeeze the fresh lemon juice over them, and serve.

Nutritional Information:

Calories: 91; Carbohydrates: 16 g; Fat: 2 g; Fiber: 8 g; Protein: 5 g; Sodium: 505 mg

ORANGE ROASTED BRUSSELS SPROUTS

Preparation time: 5 minutes; Cooking time: 10 minutes; Serves: 6

Ingredients:

- ¾ tsp. of salt
- 1 ½ lb. (454 g) quartered Brussels sprouts
- 1½ orange (cut into rings)
- 3 minced garlic cloves
- 3 tbsps. of olive oil

Instructions:

1. Let the air fryer preheat to 360ºF (182ºC).

2. Combine the quartered Brussels sprouts with olive oil, garlic, and salt so it is well coated.

3. Place the Brussels sprouts in the air fryer with the slices of orange on top, then roast for about 10 minutes.

4. Get them out of the deep fryer and keep the orange slices away. Let the Brussels sprouts sauté before serving.

Nutritional Information:

Calories: 111; Carbohydrates: 11 g; Fat: 7 g; Fiber: 4 g; Protein: 4 g; Sodium: 319 mg

CARROT AND BEAN STUFFED PEPPERS

Preparation time: 20 minutes; Cooking time: 30 minutes; Serves: 4

Ingredients:

- 2/3 (16 oz. or 454 g) can of rinsed & drained garbanzo beans

- 2/3 chopped carrot

- 2/3 large onion (chopped)

- 1/3 tsp. of black pepper (freshly ground)

- 1 tsp. of salt

- 2 cups of cooked rice

- 2 minced garlic cloves

- 2 tbsps. of extra-virgin olive oil

- 4 large bell peppers (different colors)

Instructions:

1. Let the oven preheat to 350°F (180°C or Fan 160°C).

2. Get peppers that stand upright and cut off their cap (reserve the cap for later), take out the seeds, and place them inside a baking dish.

3. Cook the carrots, olive oil, garlic, and onion in a big skillet on medium heat for about 3 minutes.

4. Add the chickpeas and cook for extra 3 minutes.

5. Take the pan off the heat and empty the contents into a big bowl.

6. Put the rice, pepper, and salt into the bowl and toss to mix.

7. Fill the peppers and cover them with the caps.

8. Use aluminum foil to cover the pan and cook for about 25 minutes.

9. Take off the foil then cook for 5 more minutes.

10. Serve while it's still hot.

Nutritional Information:

Calories: 301; Carbohydrates: 50 g; Fat: 9 g; Fiber: 8 g; Protein: 8 g; Sodium: 597 mg

ROSEMARY ROASTED RED POTATOES

Preparation time: 10 minutes; Cooking time: 20 minutes; Serves: 4

Ingredients:

- 1/3 tsp. of kosher salt
- 1/8 cup of olive oil
- 1/8 tsp. of black pepper
- 2/3 lb. (454 g) of quartered red potatoes
- 2/3 minced garlic clove
- 22/3 rosemary sprigs

Instructions:

1. Let the air fryer preheat to 360ºF (182ºC).

2. Use the olive oil, garlic, pepper, and salt to season the potatoes inside a big bowl until they are properly coated.

3. Keep the potatoes in the air fryer's basket and use the rosemary sprigs to garnish them.

4. Roast for about 10 minutes and skip or stir the potatoes then roast for 10 more minutes.

5. Take out the rosemary sprigs and serve. If necessary, season with more pepper and salt.

Nutritional Information:

Calories: 133; Carbohydrates: 12 g; Fat: 9 g; Fiber: 1 g; Protein: 1 g; Sodium: 199 mg

ZUCCHINI WITH GARLIC AND RED PEPPER

Preparation time: 5 minutes; Cooking time: 15 minutes; Serves: 4

Ingredients:

- 2/3 diced red bell pepper

- 1/3 tsp. of salt

- 11/3 medium zucchini (cubed)

- 11/3 sliced garlic cloves

- 11/3 tbsps. of olive oil

Instructions:

1. Let the air fryer preheat to 380°F (193°C).

2. Combine the olive oil, courgettes, garlic, salt, and bell pepper inside a big bowl.

3. Put the mixture inside the air fryer's basket and let it roast for about 7 minutes. Stir or shake before roasting for an additional 7 to 8 minutes.

4. Enjoy.

Nutritional Information:

Calories: 60; Carbohydrates: 4 g; Fat: 5 g; Fiber: 1 g; Protein: 1 g; Sodium: 195 mg

LEMON GREEN BEANS WITH RED ONION

Preparation time: 10 minutes; Cooking time: 10 minutes; Serves: 4

Ingredients:

- 1/3 sliced red onion
- 1/3 tsp. of salt
- 1/8 tsp. of black pepper
- 2/3 lb. (454 g) of fresh green beans (trimmed)
- 2/3 tbsp. of lemon juice
- 11/3 tbsps. of olive oil
- To serve: Lemon wedges

Instructions:

1.   Let the air fryer preheat to 360ºF (182ºC).

2.   Combine the green beans, olive oil, lemon juice, pepper, and salt.

3.   Put the mixture in the air fryer then let it roast for about 5 minutes. Mix properly and allow to cook for extra 5 minutes.

4.   Serve alongside the lemon wedges.

5.   Enjoy.

Nutritional Information:

Calories: 67; Carbohydrates: 6 g; Fat: 5 g; Fiber: 2 g; Protein: 1 g; Sodium: 199 mg

SAVORY SWEET POTATOES

Preparation time: 10 minutes; Cooking time: 18 minutes; Serves: 6

Ingredients:

- ¾ tsp. of salt

- 1/3 cup of olive oil

- 1½ tsp. of dried rosemary

- 3 large sweet potatoes (peeled & cubed)

- 3 tbsps. of shredded Parmesan

Instructions:

1. Make the air fryer preheat to 360ºF (182ºC).

2. Put sweet potatoes, rosemary, olive oil, and salt inside a large bowl and toss.

3. Transfer the sweet potatoes to the air fryer basket then roast for about 10 minutes. Stir, sprinkle the top with the shredded Parmesan and continue to roast for extra 8 minutes.

4. Serve and enjoy while it's still hot.

Nutritional Information:

Calories: 186; Carbohydrates: 13 g; Fat: 14 g; Fiber: 2 g; Protein: 2 g; Sodium: 369 mg

BEET AND WATERCRESS SALAD

Preparation time: 10 minutes; Cooking time: 10 minutes; Serves: 6

Ingredients:

- ¾ cup of water
- ¾ tsp. of table salt (add extra for seasoning)
- 1/3 cup of coarsely chopped fresh dill
- 1/3 cup of toasted, skinned, & chopped hazelnuts
- 1½ cup of plain Greek yogurt
- 1½ small, minced garlic clove
- 1½ tsp. of caraway seeds
- 1½ tbsps. of extra-virgin olive oil; divided (add extra for drizzling)
- 1½ tbsps. of white wine vinegar (divided)
- 1½ tsp. of grated orange zest
- 3 lb. (907 g) of beets (scrubbed, trimmed, & cut into ¾-inch pieces)
- 3 tbsps. of orange juice
- 7½ oz. (142 g) of watercress (torn into bite-size pieces)
- Black pepper (to taste)
- Coarse sea salt (to taste)

Instructions:

1. Mix the beets, caraway seeds, table salt, and water inside an Instant Pot. Cover with the lid, choose Manual mode, set cooking time on 8 minutes, and pressure on High. After the timer goes off, quickly release the pressure.

2. Open the lid carefully and use a slotted spoon to remove the beets. Set them on a plate and put them aside to cool a bit.

3. Mix the yogurt, 3 tbsps. of beet cooking liquid, and garlic together inside a small bowl.

4. Then toss the watercress, 1 tsp. of vinegar, and 2 tsps. of oil inside a larger bowl. Use pepper and table salt as seasoning.

5. Spread the yogurt mixture evenly over the serving dish and top with watercress, but leave a 1-inch border of the yogurt mixture.

6. Put the beets, orange juice, and zest, leftover 1 tsp. of oil, and 2 tsp. of vinegar into the emptied large bowl and toss properly. Use pepper and table salt to season to taste.

7. Neatly arrange the beets on the watercress mixture then drizzle the olive oil and sprinkle the hazelnuts, dill, and sea salt into the mixture.

8. Serve and enjoy immediately.

Nutritional Information:

Calories: 240; Carbohydrates: 19 g; Fat: 15 g; Fiber: 5 g; Protein: 9 g; Sodium: 440 mg

SIDES

BAKED ZUCCHINI STICKS

Preparation time: 10 minutes; Cooking time: 20 minutes; Serves: 6

Ingredients:

- ¼ cup of chopped parsley

- ¼ cup of crumbled feta cheese

- ¼ cup of minced garlic *Way to much, even ⅛ C - less

- ¾ cup of minced red bell pepper

- ¾ tbsp. of oregano

- ¾ tbsp. of plain salt or basil sea salt

- 1/3 cup of minced tomatoes

- 1/3 cup of pitted & minced kalamata olives

- 3 zucchinis

- Black pepper (Freshly ground)

Instructions:

1. Cut the zucchini lengthwise in half and remove the middle.

2. Mix the oregano, garlic, basil, bell pepper, olives, black pepper, and tomatoes inside a bowl.

3. Use the mixture to fill each zucchini and place them on the baking dish you prepared and bake at 250oF for up to 15 minutes.

4. Now, top it up with the feta cheese then set to broil for 3 minutes on high until it is done. Use parsley to garnish.

5.   Serve while it's still warm.

Nutritional Information:

Calories: 53; Carbohydrates: 59 g; Fat: 2 g; Fiber: 4 g; Protein: 9 g; Sodium: 138 mg

SPINACH ALMOND STIR-FRY

Preparation time: 10 minutes; Cooking time: 10 minutes; Serves: 4

Ingredients:

- 4 oz. spinach

- 2 tbsps. coconut oil

- 6 tbsps. of almond slices

- Sea or plain salt

- Black pepper (freshly ground)

Instructions:

1. Heat a skillet using coconut oil. Include the spinach and allow it to cook.

2. While it is cooking, add pepper and salt.

3. Add the almond slices.

4. Serve while it's still warm.

Nutritional Information:

Calories: 117; Carbohydrates: 59 g; Fat: 11 g; Fiber: 7 g; Protein: 3 g; Sodium: 23 mg

FRIED GREEN BEANS

Preparation time: 10 minutes; Cooking time: 15 minutes; Serves: 4

Ingredients:

- 1 lb. of trimmed green beans
- 1 tsp. of garlic powder
- 2 eggs
- 2½ tbsps. of almond flour
- 4 tbsps. of olive oil
- 4 tbsps. of parmesan cheese
- Black pepper (Freshly ground)
- Plain salt or sea salt

Instructions:

1. Beat the eggs and olive oil together inside a bowl.

2. Get a separate bowl and mix the other ingredients in it, then set it aside.

3. Dip the trimmed green beans inside the egg mixture, then dip in the dry mix to coat.

4. Grease a baking pan and put the beans inside. Bake for approximately 12 to 15 minutes at 250oF or until it gets crisp.

5. Serve while still warm.

Nutritional Information:

Calories: 334; Carbohydrates: 109 g; Fat: 23 g; Fiber: 5 g; Protein: 4 g; Sodium: 397 mg

Total Sugars: 1.9 g; Protein: 18 g

KIDNEY BEAN, VEGGIE, AND GRAPE SALAD

Preparation time: 10 minutes; Cooking time: 25 minutes; Serves: 6

Ingredients:

- ¾ cup feta cheese

- ¾ cup green pumpkin seeds (pepitas)

- ¾ cup of Dijon Red Wine Vinaigrette

- 1½ (15 oz.) can of red kidney beans, drained and rinsed

- 15 oz. of cherry tomatoes (halved or quartered if tomatoes are large)

- 2¼ cups of halved red grapes

- 3¾ oz. of baby spinach leaves (approx. 4 cups)

- 6 (6-inch) Persian cucumbers (quartered vertically & chopped)

Instructions:

1. Put the grapes, cherry tomatoes, kidney beans, pumpkin seeds, cucumbers, and feta inside a big mixing bowl to mix.

2. Put the salad mixture in cups and place them inside each of the 4 containers. Afterward, place a cup of baby spinach leaves over each salad. Then pour 2 tbsps. of vinaigrette in each one of the 4 sauce containers. Place all the containers inside a refrigerator.

3. Cover the containers and refrigerate them for 5 days.

4. Enjoy.

Nutritional Information:

Calories: 322; Carbohydrates: 37 g; Fat: 25 g; Fiber: 10 g; Protein: 16 g; Sodium: 435 mg

ROASTED PARMESAN ROSEMARY POTATOES

Preparation time: 10 minutes; Cooking time: 55 minutes; Serves: 4

Ingredients:

- ½ tsp. of salt
- 1 tsp. of garlic powder
- 2 tbsps. of olive oil
- 2 tbsps. of Parmesan cheese (grated)
- 2 tsps. of fresh rosemary (from 1 sprig) (minced)
- 24 oz. (340 g) of red potatoes (3-4 small potatoes)

Instructions:

1. Let the oven preheat to 220ºC (425º F) then place the rack in a lower position. Use parchment paper to line the baking sheet. (Avoid using foil because the potatoes would stick on them.)

2. Rub and dry the potatoes properly before cutting them into 1-inch cubes.

3. Mix the potatoes, garlic powder, olive oil, and salt inside a bowl to coat.

4. Place them on parchment paper and let them roast for about 10 minutes. Then turn them over and return to the oven for extra 10 minutes.

5. Check to make sure the top and bottom of the potatoes are golden browns, then throw them once more, reduce the heat to 180ºC, then allow to roast for additional 30 minutes.

6.   When the potatoes turn golden, cooked, and crisp, sprinkle over with Parmesan then mix them. Put back in the oven for up to 3 minutes to melt the cheese a bit.

7.   Get them out of the oven then sprinkle them over with the fresh rosemary.

8.   Enjoy.

Nutritional Information:

Calories: 193; Carbohydrates: 28 g; Fat: 8 g; Fiber: 3 g; Protein: 5 g; Sodium: 334 mg

GARLICKY ROASTED GRAPE TOMATOES

Preparation time: 10 minutes; Cooking time: 45 minutes; Serves: 4

Ingredients:

- ½ cup of olive oil

- 1 teaspoon salt

- 2 fresh rosemary sprigs

- 2 fresh thyme sprigs

- 2-pint grape tomatoes

- 20 whole garlic cloves (skins removed)

Instructions:

1.   Let the oven preheat to 350°F (180°C or Fan 160°C).

2.   Combine the tomatoes, herb sprigs, garlic cloves, oil, and salt inside a baking dish.

3.   Roast the potatoes for approximately 45 minutes, until they become soft and start caramelizing.

4.   Take out the herbs before serving and enjoy.

Nutritional Information:

Calories: 271; Carbohydrates: 12 g; Fat: 26 g; Fiber: 3 g; Protein: 3 g; Sodium: 593 mg

MEDITERRANEAN BRUSCHETTA HUMMUS PLATTER
Preparation time: 10 minutes; Cooking time: 0 minutes; Serves: 4

Ingredients:

- ¹/₃ cup of fresh tomato (finely diced)
- ¹/₃ cup of seedless English cucumber (finely diced)
- 1/8 cup of Herbed Olive Oil
- 1¹/₃ tbsps. of balsamic glaze
- 1¹/₃ tbsps. of crumbled feta cheese
- 2/3 (10 oz. or 283 g) container of plain hummus
- 2/3 tbsp. of parsley or basil (fresh chopped)
- 2/3 tsp. of extra-virgin olive oil

For serving:

- 22/3 warmed pitas (cut into wedges)
- Broccoli
- Carrot sticks
- Celery sticks
- Purple cauliflower
- Sliced bell peppers

Instructions:

1. Combine the cucumber and tomato inside a small bowl and use olive oil to drizzle over it. Stake the mixture over the new hummus container.

2. Use the balsamic glaze to season the veggies and hummus. Add the fresh parsley and crumbled feta.

3. Put the hummus over a big cutting board.

4.   Pour the olive oil into a little bowl and keep it on top of the cutting board. Use the slices of pita to surround the bowls then cut the cauliflower, carrot sticks, sliced peppers, celery sticks, and broccoli.

5.   Enjoy.

Nutritional Information:

Calories: 345; Carbohydrates: 32 g; Fat: 19 g; Fiber: 3 g; Protein: 9 g; Sodium: 473 mg

BBQ CARROTS

Preparation time: 10 minutes; Cooking time: 30 minutes; Serves: 6

Ingredients:

- ¾ tbsp. of garlic powder
- 1 tbsp. of olive oil
- 1 tbsp. of onion powder
- 1½ lb. baby carrots (organic)
- Black pepper (freshly ground)
- Plain salt or sea salt

Instructions:

1. Combine all the ingredients inside a plastic bag and coat the carrots in it completely.

2. Place an aluminum foil piece on a BBQ grill and keep the carrots on it inside a single layer.

3. Grill for about 30 minutes till the carrot gets tender.

4. Serve warm and enjoy.

Nutritional Information:

Calories: 388; Carbohydrates: 59 g; Fat: 1 g; Fiber: 4 g; Protein: 189 g; Sodium: 89 mg

LEMON GARLIC SARDINE

Preparation time: 10 minutes; Cooking time: 15 minutes; Serves: 6

Ingredients:

- ¾ cup of fresh parsley (chopped)

- ¾ tsp. of salt

- 1/3 cup of lemon juice

- 1/3 cup of parmesan cheese (finely shredded)

- 1½ cup of fresh breadcrumbs

- 3 tsp. of freshly ground pepper

- 4 oz. cans of boneless & skinless sardines (dipped in tomato sauce)

- 6 minced garlic cloves

- 6 tbsps. of extra-virgin olive oil (divided)

- 12 oz. of whole-wheat fettuccine

Instructions:

1.   Boil water into a large pot.

2.   Following the package instructions, cook the pasta for about 10 minutes until it is tender.

3.   Heat 2 tbsps. of oil in a small skillet over medium heat.

4.   Add the garlic and cook until it sizzles and becomes fragrant in approximately 20 seconds.

5.   Move the garlic to a bigger bowl.

6.   Put the leftover 2 tbsps. of oil into a skillet and heat on medium heat.

7.   Add the breadcrumbs then cook for about 5 to 6 minutes till it gets crispy and golden.

8.   Add the leftover lemon juice, pepper, and salt to the garlic bowl and whisk.

9.   Add the pasta, garlic, parmesan, parsley, and sardines to the bowl of garlic and stir gently.

10.   Let it cool then spread it over the containers.

11.   Sprinkle with the breadcrumbs before eating.

Nutritional Information:

Calories: 633; Carbohydrates: 59 g; Fat: 27 g; Fiber: 7 g; Protein: 17 g; Sodium: 771 mg

ARTICHOKE OLIVE PASTA

Preparation time: 10 minutes; Cooking time: 25 minutes; Serves: 6

Ingredients:

- ½ cup of pitted Kalamata olives (quartered lengthwise)
- ¾ cup of fresh basil leaves (torn apart)
- ¾ cup of dry white wine
- ¾ medium onion (thinly sliced)
- 1-pint grape tomatoes (halved lengthwise & divided)
- 1/3 cup of grated Parmesan cheese (plus extra for serving)
- 1½ can of artichoke hearts (drained, rinsed, & quartered lengthwise)
- 18 oz. of whole-wheat spaghetti
- 3 garlic cloves (thinly sliced)
- 3 tbsps. of olive oil (divided)
- Pepper
- Salt

Instructions:

1.   Pour salted water into a big pot to fill it up.

2.   When the water boils, follow the instructions on the package to cook the pasta until al dente.

3.   Drain but reserve a cup of the pasta's cooking water.

4.   Put the pasta back into the pot then set it aside.

5.   Heat a large skillet and pour a tbsp. of olive oil in it over medium-high heat.

6.   Add garlic and onions then use pepper and salt to season and cook until it is browned in about 3 to 4 minutes.

7.   Pour in the wine and cook until it evaporates in 2 minutes.

8.   Add the artichokes, and stir until it turns brown as it cooks for 2 to 3 minutes.

9.   Add the olives and just half of the tomatoes.

10.   Cook for 1 to 2 minutes to allow the tomatoes to break down.

11.   Put pasta into the skillet.

12.   Add the remaining tomatoes, basil, cheese, and leftover oil.

13.   Use the reserved pasta to thin the mixture if required.

14.   Put them inside containers and use the extra cheese to sprinkle.

15.   Enjoy.

Nutritional Information:

Calories: 1340; Carbohydrates: 35 g; Fat: 11 g; Fiber: 7 g; Protein: 22 g; Sodium: 334 mg

GARLIC BROCCOLI WITH ARTICHOKE HEARTS
Preparation time: 10 minutes; Cooking time: 10 minutes; Serves: 6

Ingredients:

- ¾ cup of extra-virgin olive oil (divided)

- 1½ (13¾ oz. or 390 g) can of artichoke hearts (drained & quartered)

- 1½ tsp. of red pepper flakes

- 1½ tsp. of salt

- 1½ tbsps. of water

- 3 lb. (907 g) of fresh broccoli rabe

- 3 tbsps. of red wine vinegar

- 4½ garlic cloves (finely minced)

- Black pepper (Freshly ground, to taste)

Instructions:

1.   Remove and throw away the turnip greens' yellow leaves and thick lower stems. Cut them into separate florets with some of the attached thin stems.

2.   Pour ¼ cup of olive oil inside a big skillet to heat over medium-high heat. Add the garlic, chopped broccoli, red pepper flakes, and salt then sauté it for 5 minutes and let the broccoli get soft before adding the artichoke hearts to the sauté for extra 2 minutes.

3.   Add water then lower to low heat. Cover and allow it to simmer for 3-5 minutes until the broccoli stems become tender.

4.   Whisk the remaining vinegar and ¼ cup of olive oil inside a small bowl. If desired, season the broccoli and artichokes with the ground black pepper.

5.   Serve and enjoy.

Nutritional Information:

Calories: 358; Carbohydrates: 18 g; Fat: 35 g; Fiber: 10 g; Protein: 11 g; Sodium: 918 mg

SPICY WILTED GREENS
Preparation time: 10 minutes; Cooking time: 5 minutes; Serves: 4

Ingredients:

- Pinch of salt

- 2 tbsps. of olive oil

- 4 minced garlic cloves

- 6 cups of sliced greens (spinach, kale, chard, dandelion greens, beet greens, or a mixture of all of them)

- Pinch of red pepper flakes (add more to taste)

Instructions:

1. Pour the olive oil into a skillet placed over medium-high heat. Put the garlic into the oil and sauté it until it gets fragrant in about 30 seconds.

2. Stir in the veggies, pepper flakes, and salt to mix. The veggies should wilt without overcooking. Take the pan off the heat then serve.

3. Enjoy.

Nutritional Information:

Calories: 91; Carbohydrates: 7 g; Fat: 7 g; Fiber: 3 g; Protein: 1 g; Sodium: 111 mg

BEANS

WHITE CANNELLINI BEAN STEW

Preparation time: 10 minutes; Cooking time: 30 minutes; Serves: 6

Ingredients:

- 1½ (1 lb. or 454 g) bag of baby spinach (washed)
- 1½ (15 oz. or 425 g) can of diced tomatoes
- 1½ cup of carrots (chopped)
- 1½ large onion (chopped)
- 1½ tsp. of salt
- 3 (15 oz. or 425 g) cans of white cannellini beans
- 4½ tbsps. of extra-virgin olive oil
- 6 cups of vegetable broth

Instructions:

1.   Add olive oil and onion into a large saucepan and place over medium heat to cook for 5 minutes.

2.   Stir in the beans, tomatoes, broths, carrots, and salt. Let it cook for up to 20 minutes.

3.   Add a handful of spinach at a time and continue cooking for additional 5 minutes until the spinach wilts.

4.   Serve while it's still hot.

Nutritional Information:

Calories: 356; Carbohydrates: 47 g; Fat: 12 g; Fiber: 16 g; Protein: 15 g; Sodium: 1832 mg

FRENCH GREEN LENTILS WITH CHARD
Preparation time: 15 minutes; Cooking time: 20 minutes; Serves: 4

Ingredients:

- 1/3 tsp. of grated lemon zest plus 1 tsp. of the juice

- 1/3 tsp. of table salt

- 2/3 cup of French green lentils (picked over & rinsed)

- 2/3 onion (chopped fine)

- 2/3 tsp. minced fresh thyme or 1/4 tsp. (dried)

- 11/3 minced garlic cloves

- 11/3 tbsps. of extra-virgin olive oil (add extra for drizzling)

- 11/3 tbsps. of fresh parsley (chopped)

- 12/3 cups of water

- 2 tbsps. of sliced almonds (toasted)

- 2 tbsps. of whole-grain mustard

- 8 oz. (340 g) of Swiss chard (stems chopped fine with leaves sliced into ½-inch-wide strips

Instructions:

1.   Use the maximum sauté function of your Instant Pot to heat the oil until it starts to glisten. Add the onions, chard stalks, and salt to cook for approximately 5 minutes and let the veggies soften. Add the thyme and garlic, stir and leave to cook for approximately 30 seconds so the garlic becomes fragrant. Then mix the lentils and water.

2.   Secure the lid and shut the valve for pressure release. Set on high pressure and allow to cook for up to 11 minutes before turning off the Instant Pressure and allowing it to release pressure naturally for 15 minutes. Do a quick release of the remaining pressure and take the lid off carefully to allow the steam to escape.

3.   Combine the lentils and chard leaves, a handful at a time. Let it cook for approximately 5 minutes over the residual heat until it wilts. Mix the lemon zest with juice and the mustard then use pepper and salt to season to taste. Move it to a serving dish, then drizzle the olive oil over it and sprinkle using parsley and almonds.

4.   Serve and enjoy.

Nutritional Information:

Calories: 190; Carbohydrates: 23 g; Fat: 8 g; Fiber: 6 g; Protein: 9 g; Sodium: 470 mg

ITALIAN-STYLE BAKED BEANS

Preparation time: 10 minutes; Cooking time: 15 minutes; Serves: 4

Ingredients:

- 1/3 cup of minced onion

- 1/3 cup of water

- 1/8 cup of red wine vinegar

- 1/8 tsp. of ground cinnamon

- 2/3 (12 oz. or 340 g) can of low-sodium tomato paste

- 11/3 (15 oz. or 425 g) cans of cannellini or great northern beans (undrained)

- 11/3 tbsps. of honey

- 11/3 tsps. of extra-virgin olive oil

Instructions:

1. Heat the oil inside a medium-sized saucepan placed over medium heat. Stir in the onions and cook for about 5 minutes. Then add the vinegar, tomato paste, cinnamon, honey, and water. Mix properly and turn the heat down.

2. Drain, then rinse your can of beans inside a colander, then place them inside the saucepan. Empty the second can of beans into the saucepan as well and, stirring from time to time, allow to cook for about 10 minutes.

3. Serve and enjoy.

Nutritional Information:

Calories: 290; Carbohydrates: 53 g; Fat: 2 g; Fiber: 11 g; Protein: 15 g; Sodium: 647 mg

HERB LENTIL-RICE BALLS

Preparation time: 5 minutes; Cooking time: 11 minutes; Serves: 4

Ingredients:

- 1/3 cup of cooked green lentils
- 1/3 tsp. of salt
- 1/8 cup of parsley leaves
- 1/8 minced white onion
- 2/3 cup of cooked brown rice
- 2/3 tbsp. of lemon juice
- 2/3 tbsp. of olive oil
- 11/3 minced garlic cloves
- 31/3 basil leaves

Instructions:

1.   Let the air fryer preheat to 380ºF (193ºC).

2.   Blend the garlic, cooked lentils, parsley, basil, and onion inside a food processor until it becomes smooth (Meanwhile, you'll only need some of the lentils inside the mixture).

3.   Transfer the blended mixture into a bigger bowl and add the lemon juice, brown rice, salt, and olive oil. Mix to combine.

4.   Mold the mixture to form 1-inch rice balls and arrange them in one layer inside the air fryer's basket without them touching each other.

5.   Fry one side for 6 minutes, then turn them and fry for an extra 4 to 5 minutes to ensure all sides are golden brown.

6.   Enjoy.

Nutritional Information:

Calories: 80; Carbohydrates: 12 g; Fat: 3 g; Fiber: 2 g; Protein: 2 g; Sodium: 198 mg

WHITE BEAN LETTUCE WRAPS
Preparation time: 10 minutes; Cooking time: 9 minutes; Serves: 6

Ingredients:

*   ½ cup prepared hummus or ¾ cup of lemony garlic hummus

*   ¾ cup of red onion (diced)

*   1/3 cup of fresh curly parsley (finely chopped)

*   1/3 tsp. of black pepper (freshly ground)

*   1½ (15 oz. or 425 g) can of great northern beans or cannellini (drained & rinsed)

*   1½ tbsps. of extra-virgin olive oil

*   11/8 cup of chopped fresh tomatoes

*   12 romaine lettuce leaves

Instructions:

1.   Heat oil inside a big skillet placed over medium heat. Add the diced onions and, stirring from time to time, cook for about 3 minutes. Stir in the pepper and tomatoes and cook for extra 3 minutes. Still stirring from time to time, add the beans and let it cook for 3 more minutes. Then take the skillet off the heat before adding the parsley.

2.   Spread 1 tbsp. of hummus on top of each of the lettuce leaves and top with evenly distributed hot bean mixture at the center. Fold a side of the leaf lengthwise to cover the filling, then wrap it up by folding the other side.

3.   Serve and enjoy.

Nutritional Information:

Calories: 188; Carbohydrates: 28 g; Fat: 5 g; Fiber: 9 g; Protein: 10 g; Sodium: 115 mg

BLACK-EYED PEAS SALAD WITH WALNUTS
Preparation time: 10 minutes; Cooking time: 0 minutes; Serves: 6

Ingredients:

- ¼ tsp. of pepper (add more to taste)

- ¾ cup of walnuts (toasted & chopped)

- ¾ cup of fresh parsley (minced)

- ¾ cup of pomegranate seeds

- 1/3 tsp. of salt (add more to taste)

- 3 (15 oz. or 425 g) cans of black-eyed peas (rinsed)

- 3 tbsps. of lemon juice

- 3 tbsps. of pomegranate molasses

- 4½ tbsps. of dukkha (divided)

- 4½ tbsps. of extra-virgin olive oil

- 6 scallions (thinly sliced)

Instructions:

1. Whisk the olive oil, lemon juice, and 2 tbsps. of dukkha, pomegranate molasses, pepper, and salt together inside a big bowl.

2. Add the remaining ingredients, mix, then season with pepper and salt.

3. Sprinkle the leftover spoonful of dukkha.

4. Serve and enjoy.

Nutritional Information:

Calories: 155; Carbohydrates: 12 g; Fat: 11 g; Fiber: 2 g; Protein: 2 g; Sodium: 105 mg

LENTIL STUFFED TOMATOES

Preparation time: 10 minutes; Cooking time: 15 minutes; Serves: 6

Ingredients:

- ¾ cup of cooked red lentils
- 1/3 tsp. of black pepper
- 1/3 tsp. of salt
- 1½ minced garlic clove
- 1½ tbsps. of minced red onion
- 3 tbsps. of shredded Parmesan cheese
- 6 minced basil leaves
- 6 oz. (113 g) of goat cheese
- 6 tomatoes

Instructions:

1.   Let the air fryer preheat to 380ºF (193ºC).

2.   Remove the top of the tomatoes.

3.   Cut out half part of the pulp within the tomatoes with a knife then use a spoon to create a hollow. Set each tomato inside a medium-sized bowl.

4.   Add the basil, cooked lentils, goat cheese, onion, garlic, salt, and pepper to the bowl and mix properly to combine.

5.   Spoon the mixture into each tomato's hollowed cavity then use the ½ tbsp. of grated Parmesan cheese to garnish them.

6.   Line the tomatoes up in one layer inside the air fryer's basket then cook for about 15 minutes.

7.   Serve and enjoy.

Nutritional Information:

Calories: 138; Carbohydrates: 11 g; Fat: 7 g; Fiber: 4 g; Protein: 9 g; Sodium: 317 mg

PASTA, GRAINS, & RICE
LASAGNA ROLLS

Preparation time: 10 minutes; Cooking time: 20 minutes; Serves: 4

Ingredients:

- 2/3 25-ounce can of low-sodium marinara sauce
- 1/8 teaspoon of crushed red pepper
- 1/8 teaspoon of salt
- 1/3 cup of mozzarella cheese (shredded)
- 1/3 cup of parmesan cheese (shredded)
- 2/3 tablespoon of extra virgin olive oil
- 1 14-ounces of package tofu (cubed)
- 2 tablespoons of Kalamata olives (chopped)
- 2 cups of spinach (chopped)
- 3 cloves of minced garlic
- 8 whole wheat lasagna noodles

Instructions:

1. Pour sufficient water into a large pot then follow the package instructions to cook the lasagna noodles. Afterward, drain and rinse it, then set it aside for later.

2. Sauté the garlic inside a large skillet and place it on medium heat for 20 seconds before adding the spinach and tofu. Cook until your spinach begins to wilt.

3. Put this mixture inside a bowl, then add the Parmesan olives, 2/3 cup of marinara sauce, red pepper, and salt.

4.   Spread 1 cup of marinara sauce inside a pan's bottom. Prepare the rolls by placing the noodle on a clean surface. Then spread a quarter cup of tofu filling on it. Roll it up and put it inside the pan along with your marinara sauce. Follow this procedure to roll all the lasagna noodles.

5.   Let the pan simmer over high heat. Afterward, lower to medium heat and allow to cook for additional 3 minutes. Sprinkle some mozzarella cheese on it, and give the cheese 2 minutes to melt.

6.   Serve hot and enjoy.

Nutritional Information:

Calories: 304; Carbohydrates: 39 g; Fat: 19 g; Fiber: 8 g; Protein: 23 g; Sodium: 100 mg

RED WINE RISOTTO

Preparation time: 10 minutes; Cooking time: 25 minutes; Serves: 4

Ingredients:

• ½ cup of Parmigiana-Reggiano cheese (finely shredded and divided)

• ½ medium onion (freshly chopped)

• 1/8 teaspoon of salt

• ¾ cup of Italian 'risotto' rice

• 1 cup of dry red wine

• 1 teaspoon of tomato paste

• 2 cloves of garlic (minced)

• 2 tablespoons of extra-virgin olive oil

• 2¼ cups of reduced-sodium beef broth

• Pepper (to taste)

Instructions:

1. Put broth inside a medium-sized fry pan and let it simmer over medium-high heat. Reduce the fire to make the broth steam and not simmer.

2. Heat the oil inside a Dutch oven set on medium-low heat.

3. Put onions in it to sauté for 5 minutes. Then add the garlic to cook for about 2 minutes.

4. Add the rice, season with salt, and mix properly.

5.   Add ½ cup of broth and a substantial splash of wine into the rice.

6.   Reduce to a moderate simmer and cook, stirring from time to time until the liquid in the rice is completely absorbed.

7.   Pour in another half cup of broth and a splash of wine, stirring from time to time.

8.   Stir in the tomato paste until well mixed.

9.   Keep cooking, adding more broth and wine until the broth finishes.

10.   After cooking, turn the fire off then add ¾ cup of cheese and pepper. Stir to mix.

11.   Sprinkle the remaining cheese on it and serve.

Nutritional Information:

Calories: 231; Carbohydrates: 33 g; Fat: 9 g; Fiber: 8 g; Protein: 7 g; Sodium: 100 mg

PASTA WITH FRESH TOMATO

Preparation time: 0 minutes; Cooking time: 20 minutes; Serves: 6

Ingredients:

- 1/3 cup of torn, fresh basil leaves
- 1/3 teaspoon of salt
- 1/8 teaspoon of black pepper
- 1½ cup of vertically sliced onions
- 12 ounces of sweet Italian sausage
- 12 ounces of uncooked penne (cooked & drained)
- 2 pounds of chopped tomatoes
- 3 teaspoons of minced garlic
- 3 teaspoons of olive oil
- 9 tablespoons of grated fresh pecorino Romano cheese (divided)

Instructions:

1.   Heat the oil in a non-stick fry pan placed over medium-high heat for 5 minutes. Add the sausage and onions and stir continuously until the sausage breaks into pieces.

2.   Add the garlic and stir. Allow cooking for additional 2 minutes.

3.   Add the tomatoes and continue cooking for 2 minutes.

4.   Take the pan off the fire and season with salt and pepper. Stir to mix properly.

5.   Add 2 tablespoons of cheese and the pasta. Stir and toss to mix.

6.   Place it on a serving dish then use the remaining cheese and basil to garnish before serving.

7.   Enjoy.

Nutritional Information:

Calories: 376; Carbohydrates: 50 g; Fat: 11 g; Fiber: 0 g; Protein: 17 g; Sodium: 0 mg

PESTO PASTA AND SHRIMP

Preparation time: 0 minutes; Cooking time: 15 minutes; Serves: 6

Ingredients:

- 1/3 cup of pesto (divided)

- 1/3 cup of shaved Parmesan Cheese

- 1½ cup of grape tomatoes (halved)

- 2 pounds of large shrimp (peeled & deveined)

- 4 ounces of angel hair pasta (cooked, rinsed, & drained)

Instructions:

1. Use cooking spray to grease a large non-stick fry pan placed over medium-high heat.

2. Add the shrimp, tomatoes, and pesto. Cook covered for about 15 minutes or until the shrimps become opaque.

3. Add the cooked pasta, stir, and cook until it is thoroughly heated.

4. Place on a serving plate then use the Parmesan cheese to garnish.

5. Enjoy.

Nutritional Information:

Calories: 319; Carbohydrates: 23.6 g; Fat: 11 g; Fiber: 0 g; Protein: 31.4 g; Sodium: 0 mg

CHICKEN RICE

Preparation time: 10 minutes; Cooking time: 16 minutes; Serves: 6

Ingredients:

- 2/3 small onion (chopped)
- 2/3 tablespoon of garlic (chopped)
- 2/3 tablespoons of Italian seasoning
- 1 tablespoon of olive oil
- 11/3 cups of wild rice
- 11/3 pound of chicken breast (skinless, boneless, & cut into chunks)
- 4 cups of chicken broth
- 92/3 ounces of canned cannellini beans
- Pepper
- Salt

Instructions:

1. Pour the oil into the Instant Pot's inner pot and set it on sauté mode. Add onion and garlic and leave to sauté for about 2 minutes.

2. Add the chicken and let it cook for about 2 minutes. Then add the other ingredients to your list and stir properly.

3. Cover the pot with a lid and cook for 12 minutes on high pressure.

4. When you're done, quickly release the pressure and remove the lid. Stir properly and serve.

Nutritional Information:

Calories: 399; Carbohydrates: 53.4 g; Fat: 6.4 g; Fiber: 6 g; Protein: 31.6 g; Sodium: 817 mg

FUSILLI WITH CHICKPEA SAUCE
Preparation time: 15 minutes; Cooking time: 15 minutes; Serves: 6

Ingredients:

- ¼ tsp. of black pepper (freshly ground)

- ¾ large shallot (chopped)

- 1/3 cup of extra-virgin olive oil

- 1/3 cup of fresh basil (chopped)

- 1/3 cup of shaved fresh Parmesan cheese

- 1/3 tsp. of salt

- 1½ (15 oz. or 425 g) can of chickpeas (drained & rinsed; reserve ½ cup of canning liquid)

- 1½ cup of whole-grain fusilli pasta

- 1½ tsps. of dried oregano

- 3 tsps. of dried parsley

- 7½ thinly sliced garlic cloves

- Pinch of red pepper flakes

- Red pepper flakes

Instructions:

1.   Heat oil inside a medium-sized pan placed on medium heat. Sauté the garlic and shallot in it for 3-5 minutes, or until the garlic turns golden. Add ¾ chickpeas along with 2 tbsps. of the liquid in the can. Let it simmer.

2.   Take it off the heat and place it in a standard blender. Blend properly until smooth then add the leftover chickpeas. If it gets too thick, add more of the set-aside chickpea liquid.

3.   Boil a big pot of salted water and cook the pasta for approximately 8 minutes until al dente. Reserve half a cup of the pasta water, then drain and put it back into the pot.

4.   Put the chickpea sauce into the hot pasta as well as ¼ cup of pasta water. Add more pasta water to get the preferred consistency.

5.   Put the pasta pot on medium heat, mixing intermittently until the sauce becomes thick. Use pepper and salt to season.

6.   To serve, garnish with parsley, Parmesan, red pepper flakes, basil, and oregano.

Nutritional Information:

Calories: 310; Carbohydrates: 33 g; Fat: 16 g; Fiber: 6 g; Protein: 10 g; Sodium: 243 mg

MUSHROOM FETTUCCINE

Preparation time: 10 minutes; Cooking time: 15 minutes; Serves: 6

Ingredients:

- ¾ cup of dry sherry

- ¾ tsp. of freshly ground pepper

- ¾ tsp. of salt

- 1½ cup of Asiago cheese (finely shredded; with extra for topping)

- 1½ tbsps. of extra-virgin olive oil

- 1½ tbsps. of minced garlic

- 3 cups of low-fat milk

- 3 tbsps. of all-purpose flour

- 6 cups of broccoli (divided)

- 6 cups of sliced mixed mushrooms (including cremini, oyster, etc.)

- 18 oz. of whole-wheat (or any other) fettuccine

Instructions:

1.   Boil water in a big pot and cook the pasta in it for around 8 minutes.

2.   Drain and set aside.

3.   Heat oil in a large skillet placed over medium heat.

4.   Add broccoli and mushrooms, then cook for around 8 to 10 minutes, or until the mushrooms release their liquid.

5.   Add the garlic and cook for around a minute, or until fragrant.

6.   Add sherry, but ensure you scrape any brown bits up.

7.   Allow the mix to boil for about a minute until it evaporates.

8.   Whisk flour and milk inside a separate bowl.

9.   Pour the mixture into a skillet, then season with pepper and salt.

10.   Cook for approximately 2 minutes, or until the sauce thickens and starts bubbling.

11.   Add the Asiago cheese, stirring until it melts completely.

12.   Add the sauce and toss gently.

13.   Spread over your containers. To serve, add extra cheese.

Nutritional Information:

Calories: 503; Carbohydrates: 59 g; Fat: 19 g; Fiber: 12 g; Protein: 17 g; Sodium: 1136 mg

LINGUINE WITH TOMATO SAUCE

Preparation time: 0 minutes; Cooking time: 12 minutes; Serves: 6

Ingredients:

- ¾ cup of loosely packed fresh basil leaves (torn)

- 1/3 cup of grated low-fat Parmesan cheese

- 3 cups of loosely packed baby arugula

- 3 green onions (green parts only, thinly sliced)

- 3 large vine-ripened tomatoes

- 3 tablespoons of balsamic vinegar

- 3 tablespoons of extra-virgin olive oil

- 3 tablespoons of toasted pine nuts

- 4½ ounce of low-fat Brie cheese (cubed, rind removed, & discarded)

- 12 ounces of whole wheat linguine

- Pepper (to taste)

- Salt (to taste)

Instructions:

1. Put the vinegar, Parmesan, onions, oil, basil, brie, tomatoes, arugula, salt, and pepper together inside a large bowl, toss, and set aside.

2. Following the package instructions, cook the linguine. When it is cooked, set aside 1 cup of the pasta cooking water. Drain and get rid of the remaining one but don't run the pasta under cold water. Instead, add it to the bowl of salad and allow it to sit there for a minute but do not mix.

3. Pour the ¼ cup of pasta water you reserved into the bowl to make the sauce creamy. Add more as desired then toss well to mix.

4. Serve and enjoy.

Nutritional Information:

Calories: 274; Carbohydrates: 30 g; Fat: 10 g; Fiber: 0 g; Protein: 47 g; Sodium: 0 mg

SHRIMP PAELLA MADE WITH QUINOA

Preparation time: 0 minutes; Cooking time: 40 minutes; Serves: 6

Ingredients:

- ¼ teaspoon of red pepper flakes (crushed)

- ½ cup of sliced sun-dried tomatoes (packed in olive oil)

- ½ teaspoon of black pepper

- ½ teaspoon of saffron threads (optional turmeric)

- ½ teaspoon of Spanish paprika

- ¾ cup of frozen green peas

- ¾ diced yellow onion

- ¾ pound of large shrimp (peeled, deveined, & thawed)

- ¾ red bell pepper (cored, seeded & membrane removed, then sliced into ½-inch strips)

- ¾ teaspoon of seafood seasoning

- 1 bay leaf

- 1¼ cups of dry quinoa (rinsed properly)

- 1¾ cloves garlic (minced)

- 1¾ tablespoons of olive oil

- 2½ cups of chicken broth (fat-free and low sodium)

- Salt (to taste)

Instructions:

1. Use a pinch of salt and seafood seasoning to season the shrimp. Then toss until well mixed and place in a refrigerator until you are ready to use it.

2.   Prepare the quinoa, wash and set it aside.

3.   Place a big non-stick skillet over medium-low heat. Heat the oil in it. Sauté the onions in it for 5 minutes or until it becomes tender and soft.

4.   Add the saffron (or turmeric), red pepper flakes, chicken broth, paprika, bay leaves, and quinoa. Use the pepper and salt to season.

5.   Place a lid over the skillet and allow to boil. Then reduce the heat and allow to simmer for about 10 minutes until the liquid is fully absorbed.

6.   Add the sun-dried tomatoes, shrimp, and peas, cover the lid and allow to cook for 5 minutes.

7.   Then turn the fire off and leave the paella to set for 10 minutes while the lid is still covered.

8.   Before serving, take off the bay leaf and, if desired, add a squeeze of lemon.

9.   Enjoy.

Nutritional Information:

Calories: 324; Carbohydrates: 33 g; Fat: 11.6 g; Fiber: 0 g; Protein: 22 g; Sodium: 0 mg

BUCATINI-PUTTANESCA STYLE
Preparation time: 0 minutes; Cooking time: 40 minutes; Serves: 6

Ingredients:

- ¼ teaspoon of salt

- 1½ tablespoons of rinsed capers

- 1½ teaspoons of garlic (finely chopped)

- 3 cups of whole peeled tomatoes (coarsely chopped, canned, no-salt-added) with their juice

- 3 teaspoons of fresh oregano (coarsely chopped)

- 4½ tablespoons of extra virgin olive oil, divided

- 6 anchovy fillets (chopped)

- 12 black Kalamata olives (pitted & sliced into slivers)

- 12 ounces of bucatini pasta

Instructions:

1. Following the package instructions, cook the bucatini pasta. Then drain and keep it warm. Set aside.

2. Heat 2 tablespoons of oil inside a big non-stick saucepan placed over medium heat.

3. Sauté the anchovies until they start disintegrating.

4. Add the garlic then sauté for another 15 seconds.

5. Add the tomatoes and sauté for 15-20 minutes, or until it is no longer watery. Use 1/8 teaspoon of salt to season.

6. Add the olives, oregano, and capers.

7. Add the pasta and sauté until it is heated through.

8. Drizzle the leftover olive oil on the pasta and serve.

Nutritional Information:

Calories: 207; Carbohydrates: 31.1 g; Fat: 7 g; Fiber: 0 g; Protein: 5.1 g; Sodium: 0 mg

SPAGHETTI IN AVOCADO SAUCE

Preparation time: 10 minutes; Cooking time: 30 minutes; Serves: 4

Ingredients:

- 1/8 cup of dry white wine

- 2/3 avocado, pitted and peeled 1-pound spaghetti

- 2/3 large onion (finely sliced)

- 2/3 tablespoons of olive oil

- 1 lemon (zest and juice)

- 51/3 ounces of small shrimp (shelled & deveined)

- Black pepper (freshly ground)

- Salt

Instructions:

1.   Boil water in a large pot. Then add the pasta or spaghetti and cook according to the package instructions up to al dente. Afterward, drain and set it aside.

2.   Sauté the wine and onions inside a large fry pan placed over medium heat for 10 minutes or until the onions become soft and translucent.

3.   Increase to high heat and put the shrimp inside the frying pan. Sauté constantly for about 5 minutes until the shrimp is properly cooked.

4.   Turn off the heat and season with salt. Add the oil immediately, then toss in the cooked pasta quickly. Mix properly.

5.   Puree the avocado and lemon juice inside a blender until smooth. Transfer to the frying pan containing the pasta, and mix properly.

6.   To serve, garnish with lemon zest and pepper.

Nutritional Information:

Calories: 206; Carbohydrates: 26 g; Fat: 7 g; Fiber: 8 g; Protein: 10 g; Sodium: 100 mg

RICE & SALAD

Preparation time: 10 minutes; Cooking time: 50 minutes; Serves: 6

Ingredients:

- ½ cup of dried currants
- ¾ tbsp. of lemon juice
- ¾ tsp. of cinnamon
- 1/3 cup of fresh parsley (chopped)
- 1/3 cup of olive oil
- 1½ tsp. of grated orange zest
- 11/8 cup of shelled pistachios or almonds
- 3 cups of basmati rice salt
- 3 tbsps. of fresh orange juice
- 6 green onions (chopped)
- Pepper (to taste)
- Salt (to taste)

Instructions:

1. Put the rice inside a non-stick pot placed over medium-high heat. Toast the rice for about 10 minutes until it becomes opaque and starts smelling.

2. Pour 4 quarts of boiling water into the pot and add 2 teaspoons of salt. Boil uncovered for about 8 minutes until it becomes tender.

3. Drain the rice and spread it out to cool on a lined cookie sheet.

4.   Whisk the spices, juices, and oil very well inside a big salad bowl. Add pepper and salt to taste.

5.   Add half of the parsley, and half of the green onions, nuts, and currants.

6.   Toss along with the cooled rice then leave it to stand for not less than 20 minutes.

7.   Use pepper and salt to adjust the seasoning as required.

8.   Garnish with the remaining green onions and parsley.

Nutritional Information:

Calories: 450; Carbohydrates: 50 g; Fat: 24 g; Fiber: 8 g; Protein: 9 g; Sodium: 100 mg

SHRIMP FETTUCCINE

Preparation time: 10 minutes; Cooking time: 15 minutes; Serves: 6

Ingredients:

- ¾ tsp. of black pepper (freshly ground)
- ¾ tsp. of salt
- 1/3 cup of extra-virgin olive oil
- $^1/_3$ cup of lemon juice
- 1½ lb. (454 g) of large shrimp (peeled & deveined)
- 1½ tbsps. of lemon zest
- 4½ tbsps. of minced garlic
- 12 oz. (227 g) of fettuccine pasta

Instructions:

1.   Boil a big pot of salted water. Place the fettuccine inside and cook for around 8 minutes. Set aside a half cup of the cooking liquid then drain the pasta.

2.   Heat olive oil inside a big saucepan placed over medium heat. Add garlic and sauté for a minute.

3.   Put shrimp inside the saucepan and cook both sides for around 3 minutes. Take out the shrimp and set them aside.

4.   Put the remaining ingredients inside the saucepan. Add the cooking liquid and stir before adding the pasta. Toss for an even coating with the pasta.

5.   Place the pasta on a serving dish, top with the cooked shrimp, and serve.

Nutritional Information:

Calories: 485; Carbohydrates: 50 g; Fat: 17 g; Fiber: 4 g; Protein: 33 g; Sodium: 407 mg

EASY PASTA WITH PESTO
Preparation time: 10 minutes; Cooking time: 8 minutes; Serves: 6

Ingredients:

- ¾ cup of grated Parmesan cheese

- ¾ cup of toasted pine nuts

- ¾ tsp. of black pepper (freshly ground)

- 1/3 cup of lemon juice

- 1½ cup of extra-virgin olive oil

- 1½ lb. (454 g) of spaghetti

- 1½ tsp. of salt

- 4½ cloves of garlic

- 6 cups of fresh basil leaves (stems removed)

Instructions:

1. Boil salted water inside a big pot. Add spaghetti and cook for around 8 minutes.

2. Put the remaining ingredients, apart from the olive oil, inside a food processor and pulse.

3. While it's pulsing, slowly trickle the olive oil through the opening at the top. Process until you've added all the olive oil.

4. Reserve half a cup of the cooking liquid, then drain the pasta and transfer it to a big bowl. Put the pesto and cooking liquid inside the pasta bowl as well. Toss properly.

5.   Serve instantly and enjoy.

Nutritional Information:

Calories: 1067; Carbohydrates: 91 g; Fat: 72 g; Fiber: 6 g; Protein: 23 g; Sodium: 817 mg

MUSHROOM PARMESAN RISOTTO

Preparation time: 10 minutes; Cooking time: 30 minutes; Serves: 6

Ingredients:

- ¾ cup of Parmesan cheese (freshly grated)

- ¾ tsp. of black pepper (freshly ground)

- 1½ finely chopped medium onion

- 1½ lb. (454 g) of cremini mushrooms (cleaned & sliced)

- 1½ tsp. of salt

- 2¼ cups of Arborio rice

- 3 minced garlic cloves

- 4½ tbsps. of extra-virgin olive oil (divided)

- 9 cups of vegetable broth

Instructions:

1.   Boil the broth inside a saucepan placed over medium heat.

2.   Place 1 tbsp. of olive oil along with the sliced mushrooms inside a big skillet to cook for 5 to 7 minutes over medium heat. When cooked, set the mushrooms aside.

3.   Place the same pan on medium heat and add the leftover 2 tbsps. of olive oil, garlic, and onion. Cook for around 3 minutes.

4.   Add the rice, 1 cup of broth, and salt to the pan. Combine the ingredients and cook on low heat to absorb most of the liquid. Keep stirring in half a cup of broth at a time, until it is absorbed. Do this repeatedly until you've used up all the broth.

5.   While adding the last ½ of the broth, add the Parmesan, black pepper, and cooked mushrooms. Cook for an additional 2 minutes.

6.   Serve instantly and enjoy.

Nutritional Information:

Calories: 410; Carbohydrates: 65 g; Fat: 12 g; Fiber: 3 g; Protein: 11 g; Sodium: 2086 mg

SALADS

BALSAMIC BABY SPINACH SALAD

Preparation time: 10 minutes; Cooking time: 0 minutes; Serves: 6

Ingredients:

- ¾ tsp. of fresh lemon zest
- ¾ tsp. of salt
- 1/3 cup of extra-virgin olive oil
- 1½ large ripe tomato
- 1½ lb. (454 g) of baby spinach (washed with stems removed)
- 1½ medium red onion
- 4½ tbsps. of balsamic vinegar

Instructions:

1. Slice the tomato into quarter-inch cubes. Also, cut the onion to form long slices.

2. Whisk the lemon zest, olive oil, balsamic vinegar, and salt together inside a small bowl.

3. In a larger bowl, combine the spinach, onions, and tomatoes. Add the dressing to serve.

4. Enjoy!

Nutritional Information:

Calories: 172; Carbohydrates: 9 g; Fat: 14 g; Fiber: 4 g; Protein: 4 g; Sodium: 389 mg

PISTACHIO-PARMESAN KALE & ARUGULA SALAD

Preparation time: 10 minutes; Cooking time: 0 minutes; Serves: 4

Ingredients:

- $1/3$ cup of unsalted shelled pistachios

- 1/3 tsp. of smoked paprika

- 1/8 cup of extra-virgin olive oil

- 11/3 cups of arugula

- 11/3 tbsps. of lemon juice (freshly squeezed)

- 4 cups of raw kale (center ribs removed & discarded; leaves chopped coarsely)

- 4 tbsps. of Parmesan or Pecorino Romano cheese (grated)

Instructions:

1. Mix the oil, kale, smoked paprika, and lemon juice inside a big salad bowl. Use your hands to massage the leaves gently for approximately 15 seconds, until they are fully covered. Allow the cabbage to rest for about 10 minutes.

2. Before serving, mix the pistachios and rocket gently. Then divide the salad into 6 serving bowls. Sprinkle over with 1 tbsp. of grated cheese.

3. Enjoy.

Nutritional Information:

Calories: 105; Carbohydrates: 3 g; Fat: 9 g; Fiber: 2 g; Protein: 4 g; Sodium: 176 mg

ORANGE AVOCADO & ALMOND SALAD

Preparation time: 10 minutes; Cooking time: 0 minutes; Serves: 4

Ingredients:

- 1/3 cup of honey
- 1/3 cup of sliced almonds
- 1/3 segmented & chopped oranges
- 1/3 tsp. of grated orange zest
- 2/3 large avocado (semi-ripened, medium diced)
- 2/3 tbsp. of extra-virgin olive oil
- 11/3 large chopped Gala apples

Instructions:

1. Gently mix the apples, almonds, and oranges in a big bowl.

2. Whisk the oil, honey, and orange zest inside a small bowl. Set aside.

3. Pour the mixture of orange zest on the fruit salad. Mix well before adding the avocado. Mix gently.

4. Enjoy!

Nutritional Information:

Calories: 296; Carbohydrates: 50 g; Fat: 12 g; Fiber: 7 g; Protein: 3 g; Sodium: 4 mg

ISRAELI SALAD

Preparation time: 10 minutes; Cooking time: 6 minutes; Serves: 6

Ingredients:

- ¾ cup of fresh flat-leaf Italian parsley (finely chopped)
- ¾ small red onion (finely chopped)
- 1/3 cup of extra-virgin olive oil
- 1/3 cup of pine nuts
- 1/3 cup of pistachios (shelled)
- 1/3 cup of pumpkin seeds (shelled)
- 1/3 cup of sunflower seeds (shelled)
- 1/3 cup of walnuts (coarsely chopped)
- 1/3 tsp. of black pepper (freshly ground)
- 1½ tsp. of salt
- 1½ pint of cherry tomatoes (finely chopped)
- 3 large English cucumbers (unpeeled & finely chopped)
- 3 to 3 tbsps. of lemon juice (freshly squeezed from 1 lemon)
- 6 cups of baby arugula

Instructions:

1.   Toast the walnuts, pine nuts, sunflower seeds, pumpkin seeds, and pistachios inside a big, dry skillet placed on medium-low heat for 5-6 minutes, or until fragrant and golden. Be careful not to get them burnt. Take it off the heat and put it aside.

2.   Mix the tomatoes, parsley, red onion, and cucumber inside a big bowl.

3.   Get a smaller bowl and whisk the lemon juice, olive oil, pepper, and salt together in it. Pour the mixture over the vegetables and mix well to coat.

4.   Add the toasted seeds and nuts as well as the rocket then mix very well with the salad.

5.   Serve cold or at room temperature.

Nutritional Information:

Calories: 414; Carbohydrates: 17 g; Fat: 34 g; Fiber: 6 g; Protein: 10 g; Sodium: 642 mg

TUNA SALAD

Preparation time: 10 minutes; Cooking time: 0 minutes; Serves: 6

Ingredients:

- ¾ cup of sun-dried tomatoes (thinly sliced)

- ¾ tsp. of dried cilantro

- 1/3 cup of scallions (thinly sliced; both green & white parts)

- 1/3 cup of sliced & pitted Kalamata olives

- ²/₃ cup of crumbled feta cheese

- 1½ (15 oz./425 g) can of cannellini beans (drained)

- 1½ lime (zested & juiced)

- 3 (5 oz./142 g) cans of water-packed, white albacore tuna (drained)

- 3 or 3 leaves of fresh sweet basil (thinly chopped)

- 4½ tbsps. of extra-virgin olive oil

- 6 cups of spring mix greens

- Freshly ground black pepper (to taste)

- Kosher salt (to taste)

Instructions:

1.   Mix the beans, vegetables, tuna, tomatoes, feta, olives, olive oil, scallions, coriander, lime juice & zest, and basil inside a big bowl. Use pepper and salt to season.

2.   Enjoy!

Nutritional Information:

Calories: 355; Carbohydrates: 25 g; Fat: 19 g; Fiber: 8 g; Protein: 22 g; Sodium: 744 mg

AVOCADO & HEARTS OF PALM SALAD

Preparation time: 10 minutes; Cooking time: 0 minutes; Serves: 6

Ingredients:

- ¼ tsp. of black pepper (freshly ground)

- ¾ small shallot (thinly sliced)

- 1/3 cup of flat-leaf parsley (coarsely chopped)

- 1/3 tsp. of salt

- 1½ cup of yellow cherry tomatoes (halved)

- 1½ avocado (cut into ½-inch pieces)

- 3 (14 oz./397 g) cans of hearts of palm (drained & cut into ½-inch-thick slices)

- 3 tbsps. of extra-virgin olive oil

- 3 tbsps. of low-fat mayonnaise

Instructions:

1. Mix the avocado, hearts of palm, tomatoes, parsley, and scallions inside a big bowl.

2. Meanwhile, in a smaller bowl, whisk the olive oil, mayonnaise, pepper, and salt then transfer to the large bowl and mix.

Nutritional Information:

Calories: 192; Carbohydrates: 14 g; Fat: 15 g; Fiber: 7 g; Protein: 5 g; Sodium: 841 mg

ARUGULA, WATERMELON, & FETA SALAD
Preparation time: 10 minutes; Cooking time: 0 minutes; Serves: 4

Ingredients:

- 4 oz. (57 g) of feta cheese (crumbled)

- 4 tbsps. of balsamic glaze

- 5 cups of watermelon (cut into bite-size cubes)

- 6 cups of packed arugula

Instructions:

1. Split the rocket between two plates.

2. Split the cubes of watermelon amongst the rocket beds.

3. Sprinkle 1 oz. (28 g) of the feta cheese over each salad.

4. Sprinkle approximately 1 tbsp. of frosting (add more as desired) onto each salad.

Nutritional Information:

Calories: 159; Carbohydrates: 21 g; Fat: 7 g; Fiber: 1 g; Protein: 6 g; Sodium: 327 mg

GREEK SALAD

Preparation time: 10 minutes; Cooking time: 0 minutes; Serves: 6

Ingredients:

- 6 oz. (113 g) of pitted Kalamata olives

- 1/3 cup of extra-virgin olive oil

- 1½ green bell pepper (cut into 1- to 1½-inch chunks)

- 1/3 small red onion (thinly sliced)

- 1½ tbsps. of red wine vinegar

- 1½ tbsps. of fresh oregano (chopped) or 1 tsp. of dried oregano

- 3 tbsps. of lemon juice (freshly squeezed)

- 3 large English cucumbers

- 6 Roma tomatoes (quartered)

- 1/3 tsp. of black pepper (freshly ground)

- 6 oz. (113 g) crumbled traditional feta cheese

Instructions:

1. Cut the cucumbers lengthwise in half and then cut further into ½-inch thick half-moons. Place them inside a big bowl.

2. Add the olives, quartered tomatoes, pepper, and red onion.

3. Whisk the lemon juice, olive oil, vinegar, pepper, and oregano together inside a small bowl. Sprinkle the veggies and mix well to coat.

4. Split amongst salad plates, then garnish each plate with 28 g of feta.

5.   Enjoy!

Nutritional Information:

Calories: 278; Carbohydrates: 12 g; Fat: 22 g; Fiber: 4 g; Protein: 8 g; Sodium: 572 mg

APPLE PIE POCKETS

Preparation time: 5 minutes; Cooking time: 15 minutes; Serves: 4

Ingredients:

- 1/8 cup of brown sugar
- 1/8 tsp. of ground cardamom
- 1/8 tsp. of ground cinnamon
- 2/3 Gala apple (peeled & sliced)
- 2/3 organic puff pastry (rolled out; at room temperature)
- Honey (for topping)
- Non-stick cooking spray

Instructions:

1. Let the oven preheat to 350º F (180° C or Fan 160° C).

2. Cut the shortcrust pastry into four even discs. Peel the apple and slice it. Place the slices inside a small bowl and mix with cardamom, brown sugar, and cinnamon.

3. Use a non-stick cooking spray to spray a muffin pan, ensuring you only spray the muffin stands you plan to use.

4. After sprinkling, use the batter to line the muffin mold's bottom and keep 1 or 2 broken slices of apple on top. Then fold the leftover dough over the apple slices and sprinkle the top with honey.

5. Cook for about 15 minutes, or until it becomes golden and bubbly.

6.   Serve and enjoy.

Nutritional Information:

Calories: 250; Carbohydrates: 30 g; Fat: 15 g; Fiber: 1 g; Protein: 3 g; Sodium: 98 mg

APPLE AND PLUM CAKE

Preparation time: 10 minutes; Cooking time: 40 minutes; Serves: 6

Ingredients:

- 1 grated lemon peel

- 1½ beaten egg

- 1½ tsp. of baking powder

- 3 lb. of pitted plums (cut into quarters)

- 3 pitted and chopped apples

- 4½ oz. of hot almond milk

- 7½ tbsps. of stevia

- 10 ½ oz. of almond flour

Instructions:

1.   Whisk the almond milk, stevia egg, and the remaining ingredients, apart from the cooking spray, inside a bowl until well mixed.

2.   Use oil to grease a cake pan. Then pour the cake mix into the pan, place it in an oven, and bake for 40 minutes at 350° F.

3.   Allow to cool, then slice and serve.

Nutritional Information:

Calories: 206; Carbohydrates: 8 g; Fat: 6 g; Fiber: 6 g; Protein: 6 g; Sodium: 132 mg

PANNA COTTA

Preparation time: 10 minutes; Cooking time: 35 minutes; Serves: 6

Ingredients:

- ¾ tsp. of vanilla extract
- ¾ cup. of heavy cream
- 1½ package of frozen strawberries (thawed)
- 2¼ cup. of sugar
- 2¼ envelopes of unflavoured gelatine
- 3¾ cups of milk

Instructions:

1. Mix 2 cups of milk, heavy cream, and 3/2 cup of sugar inside a saucepan. Let it come to a low simmer.

2. Put the unflavoured gelatine inside a bowl and pour the remaining ½ cup of milk over it.

3. Take the pan off the heat and add the dissolved gelatine along with the vanilla extract.

4. Pour the mixture into pudding cups and leave to chill for approximately 2 hours.

5. Mix the berries and sugar in a bowl, but don't forget to sieve to get rid of any seeds.

6. Bring to a boil over medium heat, then reduce the heat and keep on cooking for 5 minutes.

7. To serve, run a knife around each custard cup's edges to loosen it.

8.   Dribble the coulis on top and serve.

Nutritional Information:

Calories: 204; Carbohydrates: 35 g; Fat: 12 g; Fiber: 4 g; Protein: 6 g; Sodium: 100 mg

CREAM CHEESE AND RICOTTA CHEESECAKE

Preparation time: 5 minutes; Cooking time: 60 minutes; Serves: 4

Ingredients:

- ½ (16 oz. / 454 g) container of full-fat ricotta cheese
- ½ tbsp. of lemon zest
- ¾ cups of granulated sugar
- 1 (8 oz. / 227 g) package of full-fat cream cheese
- 2½ large eggs
- Non-stick cooking spray

Instructions:

1. Let the oven preheat to 350ºF (180°C or Fan 160°C).

2. Use a mixer to blend the ricotta and cream cheese.

3. Add the lemon zest and sugar. Blend.

4. Add the eggs, 1 at a time, blending for 10 seconds at a time.

5. Use the non-stick spray and parchment paper to line a 9-inch spring form pan. Use foil to wrap the pan's bottom then pour in the cheesecake mixture.

6. Make a double boiler by using a pan that is bigger than the one used for the cheesecake. Fill it with lukewarm water till it reaches about ⅓ high. Place the pan inside a double boiler and return everything to the oven. Allow the cheesecake to cool for an hour.

7.　When you're done cooking, take the pan out of the water bath and take away the foil. Allow the cheesecake to cool down on the counter for an hour. Afterward, refrigerate for not less than 3 hours before you serve.

Nutritional Information:

Calories: 489; Carbohydrates: 42 g; Fat: 31 g; Fiber: 0 g; Protein: 15 g; Sodium: 264 mg

ZUPPA INGLESE
Preparation time: 20 minutes; Cooking time: 1 hour; Serves: 6

Ingredients:

- 1 cup of espresso coffee
- 1½ teaspoons of lemon extract
- 1½ large egg
- 1½ tablespoons of butter
- 2¼ tablespoons of corn starch
- 4½ ounces of granulated sugar
- 4½ ounces of rice flour
- 8¼ ounces of ladyfingers
- 120 milliliters. of brandy
- 735 milliliters of milk

Instructions:

1. Place a big pan over medium heat, and whisk the eggs in it before adding the sugar.

2. Stir in the flour, then add corn starch and milk. Mix well.

3. When the mixture thickens, take it off the heat and leave it to cool.

4. In the meantime, prepare the espresso and allow it to cool.

5. Dip each top of the ladyfinger into the espresso before dipping it into the pan.

6.   Refrigerate.

7.   Serve when ready.

Nutritional Information:

Calories: 302; Carbohydrates: 43 g; Fat: 17 g; Fiber: 7 g; Protein: 6 g; Sodium: 33 mg

BANANA NUT CHOCOLATE CHIP MUFFINS
Preparation time: 10 minutes; Cooking time: 40 minutes; Serves: 6

Ingredients:

- 1½ large egg

- 131/8 ounces of pastry

- 2¼ ounces of chocolate chips

- 3 teaspoons of baking powder

- 4 ounces of granulated sugar

- 5¼ ounces of banana

- 93 milliliters of olive oil

- 273 milliliters of milk

Instructions:

1. Let the oven preheat to 450°F (230°C or Fan 210°C).

2. Mix the flour, baking powder, cinnamon, and sugar inside a big bowl.

3. Mash a banana (or walnuts, if desired) and add it to the bowl. Stir well.

4. Make a well at the bowl's center then add the milk, olive oil, and eggs.

5. Mix the flour mixture with the mixture at the center, but be careful not to over-mix.

6.   Put the mixture in a muffin tray.

7.   Bake for approximately 10 to 15 minutes, then allow them to cool down before you serve.

Nutritional Information:

Calories: 271; Carbohydrates: 29 g; Fat: 16 g; Fiber: 4 g; Protein: 4 g; Sodium: 51 mg

VANILLA CAKE

Preparation time: 10 minutes; Cooking time: 25 minutes; Serves: 4

Ingredients:

- ¼ cup of almond milk
- ¾ tsp. of vanilla extract
- ¾ cup of almond flour
- 1/3 cup of olive oil
- 1/3 cup of water
- 1/3 tbsp. of lime juice
- 1¼ tsps. of baking powder
- 12/3 cup of stevia
- Cooking spray

Instructions:

1. Mix the baking powder with the almond flour, oil, and the remaining ingredients, apart from the cooking spray, inside a bowl. Whisk properly.

2. Transfer the mixture to a cake pan already greased with cooking spray. Put it in the oven to bake for 25 minutes at 370° F.

3. Let the cake cool, then slice and serve.

Nutritional Information:

Calories: 200; Carbohydrates: 5 g; Fat: 7 g; Fiber: 3 g; Protein: 6 g; Sodium: 132 mg

CINNAMON AND BANANA CUPCAKES
Preparation time: 2 hours; Cooking time: 20 minutes; Serves: 6

Ingredients:

- ¾ cup of orange juice

- ¾ tsp. of baking powder

- 1½ tsps. of vanilla extract

- 11/8 cup of almond flour

- 3 peeled and chopped bananas

- 3 tsps. of cinnamon powder

- 6 eggs

- 6 tbsps. of avocado oil

- Cooking spray

Instructions:

1.   Mix the oil with orange juice, eggs, and the leftover ingredients, apart from the cooking spray, inside a bowl. Whisk properly then pour the mixture into a cupcake pan already greased with cooking spray. Bake in the oven for 20 minutes at 350° F.

2.   Let the cupcakes cool before serving.

Nutritional Information:

Calories: 142; Carbohydrates: 5 g; Fat: 5 g; Fiber: 4 g; Protein: 4 g; Sodium: 132 mg

SPANISH YOGURT CAKE
Preparation time: 20 minutes; Cooking time: 70 Minutes; Serves: 4

Ingredients:

- 1/3 of lemon juice
- 12/3 teaspoons of yeast
- 2 eggs
- 22/3 yogurt containers
- 5 ounces of yogurt

Instructions:

1. Let the oven preheat to 300°F (150°C or 130°C).

2. Crack the eggs into a mixing bowl and beat until it gets fluffy.

3. Add all the ingredients and mix until the batter gets smooth.

4. Oil a pan then fill it up with the batter (use tinfoil to cover the pan if your oven is too hot).

5. Bake for 45 to 60 minutes, or until you insert a knife into the center and it comes out dry.

6. Let it cool before serving.

Nutritional Information:

Calories: 345; Carbohydrates: 41 g; Fat: 21 g; Fiber: 5 g; Protein: 6 g; Sodium: 33 mg

CREPES

Preparation time: 15 minutes; Cooking time: 30 Minutes; Serves: 6

Ingredients:

- ¾ teaspoon of salt
- 1½ cup of flour
- 2 cups of milk
- 3 tablespoons of butter
- 3 tablespoons of sugar
- 6 eggs

Instructions:

1. Get a mixing bowl and stir in the eggs, melted butter, and milk.

2. Add the flour, salt, and sugar. Keep stirring.

3. Heat oil and butter in a pan placed over medium heat.

4. Transfer the batter to the pan and tilt it to coat the bottom surface of the pan properly.

5. Cook for 1 to 2 minutes over medium heat.

Nutritional Information:

Calories: 221; Carbohydrates: 31 g; Fat: 10 g; Fiber: 3 g; Protein: 5 g; Sodium: 335 mg

APPETIZERS AND SNACKS
SALMON ROLLS
Preparation time: 10 minutes; Cooking time: 0 Minutes; Serves: 4

Ingredients:

- 1/3 big, long cucumber (thinly sliced lengthwise)
- 1/3 tsp. of grated lemon zest
- 2/3 tsp. of dill (chopped)
- 2/3 tsp. of lime juice
- 11/3 oz. of smoked salmon (cut into strips)
- 11/3 oz. of soft cream cheese
- Black pepper (to taste)
- Salt (to taste)

Instructions:

1. Assemble the slices of cucumber on a work surface. Use a strip of salmon to cover each slice.

2. Mix the remaining ingredients in a bowl and spread the mixture over the salmon.

3. Roll the salmon and strips of cucumber up, then place them on a serving dish.

4. Serve and enjoy as an appetizer.

Nutritional Information:

Calories: 245; Carbohydrates: 16 g; Fat: 15 g; Fiber: 4 g; Protein: 17 g; Sodium: 100 mg

CUCUMBER BITES

Preparation time: 10 minutes; Cooking time: 0 Minutes; Serves: 6

Ingredients:

- ½ English cucumber (sliced into 32 rounds)
- ½ oz. of crumbled feta cheese
- ½ tbsp. of chopped parsley
- 5 oz. of hummus
- 8 cherry tomatoes (halved)

Instructions:

1. Spread the hummus over each round cucumber, then divide the tomato halves on top of each. Sprinkle the cheese and parsley on it.

2. Serve and enjoy as an appetizer

Nutritional Information:

Calories: 162; Carbohydrates: 6 g; Fat: 9 g; Fiber: 6 g; Protein: 6 g; Sodium: 283 mg

YOGURT DIP

Preparation time: 10 minutes; Cooking time: 0 Minutes; Serves: 4

Ingredients:

- 1/3 cup of olive oil

- 1/8 cup of pomegranate seeds

- 1/8 cup of za'atar spice

- 2/3 tbsp. of kalamata olives (pitted & chopped)

- 11/3 cups of Greek yogurt

- 11/3 tbsps. of chopped mint

- 11/3 tbsps. of pistachios (toasted & chopped)

- A pinch of salt

- White pepper

Instructions:

1. Mix the yogurt, pistachios, and the remaining ingredients inside a bowl. Blend until smooth then divide into smaller bowls.

2. Place pita chips on the side and serve.

Nutritional Information:

Calories: 294; Carbohydrates: 13 g; Fat: 18 g; Fiber: 18 g; Protein: 10 g; Sodium: 283 mg

LEMON MARINATED FETA & ARTICHOKES

Preparation time: 10 minutes; Cooking time: 0 Minutes; Serves: 1½ cups

Ingredients:

- ½ tsp. of black peppercorns
- ⅓ cup of extra-virgin olive oil
- 1 lemon (zest and juice)
- 2 tbsps. of fresh parsley (roughly chopped)
- 2 tbsps. of fresh rosemary (roughly chopped)
- 4 oz. (113 g) of drained artichoke hearts (quartered lengthwise)
- 4 oz. (113 g) of traditional Greek feta (cut into ½-inch cubes)

Instructions:

1. Mix the artichoke hearts and feta inside a large glass jar or glass bowl.

2. Add the lemon zest and juice, olive oil, rosemary, peppercorns, and parsley and mix gently until coated, but do not crumble the feta.

3. Cover the jar or bowl and place in a fridge for not less than 4 hours or as long as 4 days. Remove from the refrigerator 30 minutes before serving.

Nutritional Information:

Calories: 235; Carbohydrates: 3 g; Fat: 23 g; Fiber: 1 g; Protein: 4 g; Sodium: 406 mg

CREAMY HUMMUS

Preparation time: 10 minutes; Cooking time: 0 Minutes; Serves: 4

Ingredients:

- ¼ cup of tahini paste
- ½ (15 oz./425 g) can of garbanzo beans (rinsed & drained)
- ½ tsp. of salt
- 1/8 cup of lemon juice
- 1/8 cup of plain Greek yogurt
- 1 peeled garlic clove
- 1 tbsp. of extra-virgin olive oil (divided)

Instructions:

1. Get a food processor with a chopping blade and put the garlic cloves, chickpeas, lemon juice, and salt in it. Blend for a minute or until smooth.

2. Scrape all the sides of the processor. Then add the Greek yogurt, 1 tbsp. of olive oil, and tahini pastes and blends for 1 more minute, or until it is creamy and very smooth.

3. Pour into a serving bowl. Drizzle the leftover spoonful of olive oil over it.

4. Serve and enjoy.

Nutritional Information:

Calories: 189; Carbohydrates: 14 g; Fat: 13 g; Fiber: 4 g; Protein: 7 g; Sodium: 313 mg

STUFFED AVOCADO

Preparation time: 10 minutes; Cooking time: 0 Minutes; Serves: 4

Ingredients:

- 2 avocados (halved & pitted)
- 2 tbsps. of basil (chopped)
- 3 tbsps. of basil pesto
- 4 tbsps. of black olives (pitted & chopped)
- 4 tbsps. of sun-dried tomatoes (chopped)
- 4 tsps. of pine nuts (toasted & chopped)
- 20 oz. of canned tuna (drained)
- Black pepper (to taste)
- Salt (to taste)

Instructions:

1. Mix the tuna, sun-dried tomatoes, and the remaining ingredients, apart from the avocado, inside a bowl. Combine well.

2. Stuff the individual avocado halves with the mixture.

3. Serve and enjoy as an appetizer.

Nutritional Information:

Calories: 233; Carbohydrates: 11 g; Fat: 9 g; Fiber: 6 g; Protein: 6 g; Sodium: 283 mg

TOMATO BRUSCHETTA

Preparation time: 10 minutes; Cooking time: 10 Minutes; Serves: 4

Ingredients:

- ¼ cup of basil (chopped)

- 1/3 tsp. of garlic powder

- 2/3 tbsp. of balsamic vinegar

- 2/3 tsp. of olive oil

- 4 sliced baguettes

- 6 tomatoes (cubed)

- A pinch of salt

- Black pepper

- Cooking spray

- Minced garlic cloves

Instructions:

1. Place the slices of baguette on a baking sheet already lined with parchment paper. Use the cooking spray to grease them and bake for 10 minutes at 200° C.

2. Mix the tomatoes, basil, and other remaining ingredients inside a bowl. Mix properly and set to the side for 10 minutes.

3. Split the tomato sauce onto each baguette slice; assemble them on a serving plate.

4. Serve and enjoy.

Nutritional Information:

Calories: 162; Carbohydrates: 29 g; Fat: 4 g; Fiber: 18 g; Protein: 4 g; Sodium: 283 mg

SWEET POTATO CHIPS

Preparation time: 5 minutes; Cooking time: 15 Minutes; Serves: 4

Ingredients:

- ¼ tsp. of salt

- 2 large sweet potatoes (thinly sliced)

- 4 tbsps. of olive oil

Instructions:

1. Let the air fryer preheat to 380ºF (193ºC).

2. Mix the sweet potatoes, olive oil, and salt inside a small bowl. Ensure the potatoes are coated very well.

3. Place the slices of sweet potato in the air fryer, rolled out in a single layer.

4. Fry for about 10 minutes. Stir and air fry for an additional 3 to 5 minutes, or until they are as crunchy as you would like.

Nutritional Information:

Calories: 175; Carbohydrates: 13 g; Fat: 14 g; Fiber: 2 g; Protein: 1 g; Sodium: 191 mg

KALAMATA OLIVE TAPENADE

Preparation time: 10 minutes; Cooking time: 0 Minutes; Serves: 2 cups

Ingredients:

- ¼ cup of extra-virgin olive oil
- 1 cooked egg yolk
- 1 garlic clove (finely minced)
- 1 tsp. of Dijon mustard
- 2 anchovy fillets (chopped)
- 2 cups of pitted Kalamata olives (or other black olives)
- 2 tsps. of chopped capers
- For serving: Vegetables (optional)

Instructions:

1. Mix the olives, orange zest and juice, vinegar, oil, bay leaves, garlic, chili flakes, allspice, and cumin inside a glass jar or big bowl. Mix properly.

2. Cover and place in a refrigerator for a minimum of 4 hours or a maximum of 1 week to enable the olives to marinate. Turn them one more time before serving.

Nutritional Information:

Calories: 179; Carbohydrates: 3 g; Fat: 19 g; Fiber: 2 g; Protein: 2 g; Sodium: 812 mg

CITRUS GARLIC MARINATED OLIVES

Preparation time: 10 minutes; Cooking time: 0 Minutes; Serves: 2 cups

Ingredients:

- ¼ cup of extra-virgin olive oil
- ¼ cup of red wine vinegar
- ½ tsp. of ground allspice
- ½ tsp. of ground cumin
- 1 tsp. of red pepper flakes
- 2 bay leaves
- 2 cups of mixed green olives (with pits)
- 4 finely minced garlic cloves
- Zest & juice of 1 large orange or 2 clementines

Instructions:

1. Combine the orange zest & juice, olives, oil, vinegar, garlic, bay leaves, red pepper flakes, allspice, and cumin inside a large jar or glass bowl. Mix properly.

2. Cover and place in the fridge for a minimum of 4 hours or a maximum of a week to enable the olives to marinate.

3. Toss once more before serving.

Nutritional Information:

Calories: 133; Carbohydrates: 3 g; Fat: 14 g; Fiber: 2 g; Protein: 1 g;
Sodium: 501 mg

HOLIDAY & PIZZA RECIPES
TUNA PIZZA
Preparation time: 15 minutes; Cooking time: 25 Minutes; Serves: 4

Ingredients:

- 1/3 cup of red onion (minced)
- 1 cup of grated mozzarella cheese
- 31/3 ounce can of tuna (drained well & flaked)
- 51/3 ounce package of cream cheese (softened)
- 91/3 ounce package of prebaked pizza crust
- Smashed red pepper flakes

Instructions:

1. Let the oven preheat to 400°F (200°C or Fan 180°C).

2. Share the cream cheese evenly on the dough.

3. Use tuna, red pepper flakes, onions, and mozzarella to garnish.

4. Bake for about 15 to 20 minutes, or until your pizza crust becomes browned and bubbly.

Nutritional Information:

Calories: 314; Carbohydrates: 47 g; Fat: 12 g; Fiber: 8 g; Protein: 17 g; Sodium: 572 mg

ESCAROLE PIZZA

Preparation time: 15 minutes; Cooking time: 35 Minutes; Serves: 6

Ingredients:

- 1½ tablespoons of olive oil
- 1½ chopped garlic clove
- 1½ prepared pizza crust
- 2¼ cups of pizza sauce
- 3 cups of grated mozzarella cheese
- 7½ escarole leaves (soak-drain)
- Pepper
- Salt

Instructions:

1. Let the oven preheat to 350°F (180°C or Fan 160°C).

2. Rub oil on the crust finely then spread the pizza sauce, seasoning it with garlic.

3. Take off the stiff escarole stems; place the leaves on the pizza, garnished with the mozzarella.

4. Bake for around 25 to 30 minutes, or until the cheese is melted.

5. Serve immediately.

Nutritional Information:

Calories: 289; Carbohydrates: 51 g; Fat: 15 g; Fiber: 5 g; Protein: 13 g; Sodium: 572 mg

VEGGIE PIZZA SQUARES
Preparation time: 15 minutes; Cooking time: 20 Minutes; Serves: 6

Ingredients:

* ½ cup of sour cream

* 1½ teaspoon of dry dill

* 1½ can of crescent rolls

* 2¼ teaspoon of garlic powder

* 3 cups of chopped mixed veggies

* 3 teaspoons of lemon juice

* 9 ounces of cream cheese

* 9 ounces of crumbled feta cheese

Instructions:

1. Oil a skillet and arrange crescent rolls in it and cook according to the package instructions. Allow cooling completely.

2. Mix the lemon juice, cream cheese, sour cream, garlic powder, and dill in a small bowl and whisk until it becomes smooth.

3. Share the mixture on the crusts and use the chopped vegetables and feta cheese to garnish it.

4. Slice into squares and serve immediately.

Nutritional Information:

Calories: 377; Carbohydrates: 45 g; Fat: 15 g; Fiber: 8 g; Protein: 14 g; Sodium: 572 mg

HOLIDAY CAPPUCCINO

Preparation time: 15 minutes; Cooking time: 10 Minutes; Serves: 6

Ingredients:

- 1½ fluid ounces vanilla extract
- 1½ teaspoons of chocolate shavings
- 3 fluid ounces of amaretto liqueur
- 3 fluid ounces of brandy
- 6 teaspoons of instant hot chocolate mix
- 6 teaspoons of whipped cream
- 6 teaspoons of white sugar
- 18 fluid ounces half-and-half
- 18 fluid ounces hot brewed espresso

Instructions:

1.   Whisk some hot espresso, half-and-half, brandy, and amaretto together inside a medium-size saucepan on medium-low heat.

2.   Add the vanilla extract and hot chocolate. Mix well before adding sugar.

3.   Cook until the sugar dissolves completely.

4.   Finally, divide the chocolate mixture into 4 mugs and top with either whipped cream or some other chocolate shavings.

5.   Serve.

Nutritional Information:

Calories: 162; Carbohydrates: 4 g; Fat: 8 g; Fiber: 4 g; Protein: 8 g; Sodium: 572 mg

ARTICHOKE CAPRESE PLATTER
Preparation time: 20 minutes; Cooking time: 0 Minutes; Serves: 6

Ingredients:

- 1½ pounds of mozzarella cheese (diced)

- 3 cups of basil leaves

- 3 tablespoons of olive oil

- 3 tablespoons of red wine vinegar

- 9 plum tomatoes (diced)

- 22½ ounces of marinated artichokes

- Coarsely ground pepper

Instructions:

1. Let the artichokes drain then set aside ½ cup of marinade

2. Whisk the vinegar, reserved marinade, and oil inside a small bowl.

3. Organize the artichokes, basil, mozzarella cheese, and tomatoes on top of a big serving plate.

4. Drizzle the top with vinaigrette and use coarsely ground pepper to season as preferred. Serve.

Nutritional Information:

Calories: 2180; Carbohydrates: 6 g; Fat: 4 g; Fiber: 4 g; Protein: 1 g; Sodium: 100 mg

ITALIAN FARFALLE
Preparation time: 15 minutes; Cooking time: 30 Minutes; Serves: 6

Ingredients:

- ¾ cup of basil leaves

- ¾ cup of olive oil

- ¾ cup of Parmesan cheese (shredded)

- ¾ cup of pine nuts

- ¾ cup of red wine vinegar

- 1½ cup of chopped tomato

- 1½ pounds crumbles of chorizo sausage

- 3 cloves of garlic (minced)

- 18 ounces farfalle pasta

Instructions:

1. Boil pasta inside salted water.

2. Simultaneously while cooking the pasta, brown the chorizo on medium heat. Go on to add the nuts but ensure you don't let them burn. Take the pan off the heat then add garlic.

3. Get the pasta out of the pot and transfer it to a large bowl. Toss the pasta, chorizo mixture, tomatoes, cheese, and basil together inside the bowl.

4. Mix the vinegar and olive oil; pour the mixture over the pasta, toss and serve.

Nutritional Information:

Calories: 365; Carbohydrates: 60 g; Fat: 11 g; Fiber: 4 g; Protein: 10 g; Sodium: 100 mg

SKEWERS

Preparation time: 25 minutes; Cooking time: 0 Minutes; Serves: 6

Ingredients:

- 16 ounces of mozzarella cheese
- 24 pimiento-stuffed Queen olives
- 24 thin slices of ½ pounds of hard salami
- 48 grape tomatoes
- Italian vinaigrette

Instructions:

1. Thread the tomatoes, salami slices, mozzarella, and olives on wooden skewers.

2. Place in a refrigerator until all is set to serve. Sprinkle vinaigrette on the skewers before serving.

Nutritional Information:

Calories: 240; Carbohydrates: 7 g; Fat: 6 g; Fiber: 1 g; Protein: 4 g; Sodium: 100 mg

EASY CUCUMBER SANDWICHES

Preparation time: 25 minutes; Cooking time: 0 Minutes; Serves: 6

Ingredients:

- 3 tablespoons of mayonnaise
- 3 teaspoons of Italian salad dressing
- 12 ounces of softened cream cheese
- 45 slices of pumpernickel bread
- 90 thin cucumber slices
- Dill springs
- Slivered red pearl onions

Instructions:

1.   Mix the cream cheese and mayonnaise with the dressing in a medium bowl. Set aside for about 30 minutes.

2.   Divide the cream cheese mixture and spread it on the 2 slices of bread.

3.   Use the 2 cucumber slices, red onion slivers (optional), and dill as toppings.

4.   Place in the fridge until you are ready to serve.

Nutritional Information:

Calories: 287; Carbohydrates: 15 g; Fat: 9 g; Fiber: 3 g; Protein: 9 g; Sodium: 100 mg

12-WEEK FLEXIBLE MEAL PLAN

The Mediterranean diet is more than just a fad diet; it's a way of life. The best way to reap the benefits of this healthy eating style is to incorporate it into your daily routine.

Here's a 12-weeks-long meal plan that will help get you started:

WEEK 1

	Mon	Tue	Wed	Thurs	Fri	Sat	Sun
Breakfast	Banana corn fritters	Sweet potato toast	Cheese Frittata with vegetables	Green smoothie	Pancakes with berry sauce	Cardamom-cinnamon oats	Greek yogurt with nuts
Lunch	Salmon with tomatoes	Greek chicken rice	Lemon rosemary branzino	Chicken and olives	Fideos with seafood	White cannellini bean stew	Fish fillet on lemons
Snacks	Salmon rolls	Cucumber bites	Yogurt dip	Lemon marinated feta & artichokes	Creamy hummus	Stuffed avocado	Tomato bruschetta
Dinner	Peach-glazed chicken drumsticks	Roasted shrimp-gnocchi bake	Beef kofta	Fast seafood paella	Chicken meatballs with parmesan	Garlic shrimp black bean pasta	Moroccan chicken meatballs

WEEK 2

	Mon	Tue	Wed	Thurs	Fri	Sat	Sun
Breakfast	Bulgur bowls with fruits	Bruschetta with prosciutto	Ricotta with honey	Poached eggs	Blueberry and chia seeds smoothie	Orange French toast	Vanilla raspberry oats
Lunch	Fish and orzo	Yogurt-marinated chicken	Italian fried shrimp	Traditional chicken shawarma	Thyme whole roasted red snapper	Lemon-garlic whole chicken & potatoes	French green lentils with chard
Snacks	Sweet potato chips	Kalamata olive tapenade	Citrus garlic marinated olives	Salmon rolls	Cucumber bites	Yogurt dip	Lemon marinated feta & artichokes
Dinner	Parsley-dijon chicken and potatoes	Crispy artichokes with lemon	Poached chicken breast with romesco sauce	Crispy fried sardines	Sautéed cabbage	Shrimp with garlic and mushrooms	Peach-glazed chicken drumsticks

WEEK 3

	Mon	Tue	Wed	Thurs	Fri	Sat	Sun
Breakfast	Avocado with eggs toast	Banana corn fritters	Sweet potato toast	Cheese Frittata with vegetables	Green smoothie	Pancakes with berry sauce	Cardamom-cinnamon oats
Lunch	Chicken shish tawook	Orange roasted brussels sprouts	Chicken meatballs with parmesan	Carrot and bean stuffed peppers	Moroccan chicken meatballs	Rosemary roasted red potatoes	Poached chicken breast with romesco sauce
Snacks	Creamy hummus	Stuffed avocado	Tomato bruschetta	Sweet potato chips	Kalamata olive tapenade	Citrus garlic marinated olives	Salmon rolls
Dinner	Beet and watercress salad	Moroccan chicken thighs and vegetable tagine	Italian-style baked beans	Lentil stuffed tomatoes	Lasagna rolls	Fusilli with chickpea sauce	Herb lentil-rice balls

WEEK 4

	Mon	Tue	Wed	Thurs	Fri	Sat	Sun
Breakfast	Greek yogurt with nuts	Bruschetta with prosciutto	Ricotta with honey	Poached eggs	Blueberry and chia seeds smoothie	Orange French toast	Vanilla raspberry oats
Lunch	Turkey bacon bites	Zucchini with garlic and red pepper	Grilled beef kebabs	Lemon green beans with red onion	Pork wraps	Savory sweet potatoes	Mediterranean lamb bowls
Snacks	Cucumber bites	Yogurt dip	Lemon marinated feta & artichokes	Creamy hummus	Stuffed avocado	Tomato bruschetta	Sweet potato chips
Dinner	White bean lettuce wraps	Red wine risotto	Black-eyed peas salad with walnuts	Pasta with fresh tomato	Greek lemon chicken kebabs	Pesto pasta and shrimp	Chicken rice

WEEK 5

	Mon	Tue	Wed	Thurs	Fri	Sat	Sun
Breakfast	Avocado with eggs toast	Banana corn fritters	Sweet potato toast	Cheese Frittata with vegetables	Green smoothie	Pancakes with berry sauce	Cardamom-cinnamon oats
Lunch	Fusilli with chickpea sauce	Salmon with tomatoes	Linguine with tomato sauce	Roasted shrimp-gnocchi bake	Shrimp paella made with quinoa	Lemon rosemary branzino	Mushroom fettuccine
Snacks	Kalamata olive tapenade	Citrus garlic marinated olives	Salmon rolls	Cucumber bites	Yogurt dip	Lemon marinated feta & artichokes	Creamy hummus
Dinner	White cannellini bean stew	Salmon with tomatoes	Shrimp with garlic and mushrooms	French green lentils with chard	Roasted shrimp-gnocchi bake	Thyme whole roasted red snapper	Italian-style baked beans

WEEK 6

	Mon	Tue	Wed	Thurs	Fri	Sat	Sun
Breakfast	Greek yogurt with nuts	Bruschetta with prosciutto	Ricotta with honey	Poached eggs	Blueberry and chia seeds smoothie	Orange French toast	Vanilla raspberry oats
Lunch	Fast seafood paella	Herb lentil-rice balls	Lemon rosemary branzino	Fideos with seafood	White bean lettuce wraps	Fast seafood paella	Garlic shrimp black bean pasta
Snacks	Stuffed avocado	Tomato bruschetta	Sweet potato chips	Kalamata olive tapenade	Citrus garlic marinated olives	Salmon rolls	Cucumber bites
Dinner	Bucatini-puttanesca style	Avocado & hearts of palm salad	Spaghetti in avocado sauce	Greek salad	Rice & salad	Arugula, watermelon, & feta salad	Shrimp fettuccine

WEEK 7

	Mon	Tue	Wed	Thurs	Fri	Sat	Sun
Breakfast	Avocado with eggs toast	Banana corn fritters	Sweet potato toast	Cheese Frittata with vegetables	Green smoothie	Pancakes with berry sauce	Cardamom-cinnamon oats
Lunch	Easy pasta with pesto	Fish fillet on lemons	Mushroom parmesan risotto	Black-eyed peas salad with walnuts	Fish and orzo	Fideos with seafood	Lentil stuffed tomatoes
Snacks	Salmon rolls	Cucumber bites	Yogurt dip	Lemon marinated feta & artichokes	Creamy hummus	Stuffed avocado	Tomato bruschetta
Dinner	Balsamic baby spinach salad	Orange avocado & almond salad	Tuna salad	Pistachio-parmesan kale & arugula salad	Israeli salad	Crispy fried sardines	Orange avocado & almond salad

WEEK 8

	Mon	Tue	Wed	Thurs	Fri	Sat	Sun
Breakfast	Greek yogurt with nuts	Bruschetta with prosciutto	Ricotta with honey	Poached eggs	Blueberry and chia seeds smoothie	Orange French toast	Vanilla raspberry oats
Lunch	Italian fried shrimp	Moroccan chicken thighs and vegetable tagine	Lasagna rolls	Shrimp with garlic and mushrooms	Yogurt-marinated chicken	Red wine risotto	Thyme whole roasted red snapper
Snacks	Sweet potato chips	Kalamata olive tapenade	Citrus garlic marinated olives	Salmon rolls	Cucumber bites	Yogurt dip	Lemon marinated feta & artichokes
Dinner	Greek chicken rice	Israeli salad	Pasta with fresh tomato	Pesto pasta and shrimp	Tuna salad	Chicken and olives	Avocado & hearts of palm salad

WEEK 9

	Mon	Tue	Wed	Thurs	Fri	Sat	Sun
Breakfast	Avocado with eggs toast	Banana corn fritters	Sweet potato toast	Cheese Frittata with vegetables	Green smoothie	Pancakes with berry sauce	Cardamom-cinnamon oats
Lunch	Traditional chicken shawarma	Chicken rice	Lemon-garlic whole chicken and potatoes	Fusilli with chickpea sauce	Mushroom fettuccine	Bucatini-puttanesca style	Chicken shish tawook
Snacks	Salmon rolls	Cucumber bites	Yogurt dip	Lemon marinated feta & artichokes	Creamy hummus	Stuffed avocado	Tomato bruschetta
Dinner	Arugula, watermelon, & feta salad	Chicken meatballs with parmesan	Linguine with tomato sauce	Greek salad	Shrimp paella made with quinoa	Greek lemon chicken kebabs	Easy cucumber sandwiches

WEEK 10

	Mon	Tue	Wed	Thurs	Fri	Sat	Sun
Breakfast	Greek yogurt with nuts	Bruschetta with prosciutto	Ricotta with honey	Poached eggs	Blueberry and chia seeds smoothie	Orange French toast	Vanilla raspberry oats
Lunch	Moroccan chicken meatballs	Spaghetti in avocado sauce	Garlic shrimp black bean pasta	Poached chicken breast with romesco sauce	Rice & salad	Fish fillet on lemons	Peach-glazed chicken drumsticks
Snacks	Sweet potato chips	Kalamata olive tapenade	Citrus garlic marinated olives	Salmon rolls	Cucumber bites	Yogurt dip	Lemon marinated feta & artichokes
Dinner	Turkey bacon bites	Savory sweet potatoes	Shrimp fettuccine	Balsamic baby spinach salad	Beet and watercress salad	Skewers	Veggie pizza squares

WEEK 11

	Mon	Tue	Wed	Thurs	Fri	Sat	Sun
Breakfast	Avocado with eggs toast	Banana corn fritters	Sweet potato toast	Cheese Frittata with vegetables	Green smoothie	Pancakes with berry sauce	Cardamom-cinnamon oats
Lunch	Grilled beef kebabs	Easy pasta with pesto	Pork wraps	Fish and orzo	Chicken meatballs with parmesan	Mediterranean lamb bowls	Mushroom parmesan risotto
Snacks	Salmon rolls	Cucumber bites	Yogurt dip	Lemon marinated feta & artichokes	Creamy hummus	Stuffed avocado	Tomato bruschetta
Dinner	Carrot and bean stuffed peppers	Rosemary roasted red potatoes	Zucchini with garlic and red pepper	Beef kofta	Lemon green beans with red onion	Italian farfalle	Escarole pizza

WEEK 12

	Mon	Tue	Wed	Thurs	Fri	Sat	Sun
Breakfast	Greek yogurt with nuts	Bruschetta with prosciutto	Ricotta with honey	Poached eggs	Blueberry and chia seeds smoothie	Orange French toast	Vanilla raspberry oats
Lunch	Moroccan chicken meatballs	Crispy fried sardines	Parsley-dijon chicken and potatoes	Greek chicken rice	Chicken and olives	Italian fried shrimp	Poached chicken breast with romesco sauce
Snacks	Sweet potato chips	Kalamata olive tapenade	Citrus garlic marinated olives	Salmon rolls	Cucumber bites	Yogurt dip	Lemon marinated feta & artichokes
Dinner	Sautéed cabbage	Peach-glazed chicken drumsticks	Crispy artichokes with lemon	Pistachio-parmesan kale & arugula salad	Orange roasted brussels sprouts	Artichoke Caprese platter	Tuna pizza